CAT BOOK

The complete book of cat and kitten care

Written by Veterinary Surgeons

Illustrated by Judy Friedlander and Gillian Croucher

For further information, contact Sherley's at Beaphar UK Ltd,
Homefield Road, Haverhill, Suffolk, CB9 8QP, Telephone: (01440) 715700
www.sherleys.com

ABOUT THIS BOOK

Although the cat is one of the most popular domesticated pets, it often remains aloof from its human owner, treating its home merely as a convenience between forays outside. Unlike the gregarious dog, cats are more solitary and participate only on their own terms. But they are capable of great affection and friendship of a type that many people find preferable to that of their boisterous canine cousins.

This book is written with a full sympathetic understanding of the way cats are and is intended to provide a complete manual of cat care. It is the companion volume to the 'Sherley's Dog Book'. As with dogs, the name Sherley's has been closely associated with health and care of cats for almost a century. Sherley's 'Hints to Cat Lovers', as it was then known, was first published in 1925 and has been through many revisions since then. This edition has been written by Veterinary Surgeons and it is right up-to-date in its views on cat care and takes full account of current practice in Veterinary medicines and surgery.

The first chapter is devoted to choosing and knowing your cat, the second deals with kittening, and the following three chapters cover all aspects of rearing and caring for kittens and adult cats.

The second half of the book is concerned primarily with health. It covers parasites, treatment and first aid, diseases and ailments, ending with notes on Sherley's cat care products. Whilst the book emphasises the role that the owner can play in keeping a cat fit and healthy, it never fails to point out that, except in simple cases, most health problems should be quickly referred to a Veterinary Surgeon.

This is a book for all who care about cats, whether they are cat owners, about to acquire their first cat, or just cat lovers.

CHAPTER		Page

35th Edition 2002

Printed in the Netherlands by Hassink Drukkers B.V. - Haaksbergen.

CHAPTER 1

CHOOSING AND KNOWING YOUR CAT

Cats have been established as household pets and friends of man for many thousands of years. The ancient Egyptians revered them and their ceremonially mummified remains have been found with those of their owners in the pyramids. However, if the "Just So" stories of Kipling are to be believed, the cat was the last of the animals to accept domestication in exchange for the warmth of the camp fire and to this day most cats retain a certain aloofness in their affection for their owners, rather than the unquestioning devotion of dogs.

It was probably the Romans who first introduced the cat to Britain, although there was, and still is, a native wild cat in Scotland that has never been domesticated. In the middle ages, the enthusiasm for cats rather declined and probably few were kept as pets, but they were valued for their ability to catch rats and mice and a manuscript of that time quotes the current price for a mousing cat somewhere between a farthing and a halfpenny.

The popular pet

However, today cats seem to be at a peak of popularity in the civilised world. It seems that no calendar, poster, or advertisement is complete unless a cat is included somewhere. They can be used to promote almost anything. It may be an elegant Siamese, a fluffy Persian kitten, or just an ordinary everyday cross-bred cat, but there is somehow charm in the totally characteristic attitudes and behaviour, a cattiness in the nicest sense of the word, that makes cat lovers everywhere stop and smile and look again.

Shows

While it is probably true to say that cat shows are more fun for owners than for cats, competitive shows (run under the auspices of the National Cat Club and the Governing Council of the Cat Fancy) have done much to popularise cats as pets and to encourage a proper sense of concern for their welfare. These shows were first started towards the end of the last century and both Queen Victoria and Edward VII were known to attend. At that time prizes were awarded for the fattest and heaviest cats, but today we have a more rational appreciation of show points and most owners realise that cats should be sleek and healthy but not overweight.

Cat plusses

Today's changing circumstances, when in many households people are out at work all day, make the cat especially suitable as a family pet. They do not need exercising when you come home tired at night. They are ideal for busy people (or lazy people) or for the elderly who love to have a pet, but can no longer manage the long walks that a dog needs. They can be left alone in the house throughout the day; after all they sometimes sleep quite happily for twelve hours at a time if it suits them whether their owners are in or not. They do not bark or create a disturbance to annoy neighbours, and these days when pets in towns are getting so much adverse publicity it is worth remembering that cats do not foul footpaths (although it is true that they do sometimes dig up flowerbeds).

Costs

Feeding costs are low, or at least they should be. It is true that some owners spend large sums on costly delicacies for their cats but this is more for their own pleasure and satisfaction than from any real need to do so. A healthy cat that has been sensibly reared will keep fit and contented on the good quality tinned or dried foods that are available today. Faddy cats are, as a rule, those that have been overfed.

One or two?

Having made a point that one cat in the home is a good thing, why not consider having two? There is no doubt that in most cases a cat's life is more enjoyable if there is another cat in the house and their games and scraps and the interplay of relationships between the two provide endless amusement and entertainment for their owners.

Insurance

However, while feeding costs should not be high it is important to remember before embarking on too large a family that veterinary costs today may be a considerable item and accidents and illnesses occur when they are least expected; health-wise, two cats definitely cost more than one. It is advisable that you consider taking out an insurance policy that will provide financial help should your pet suffer a serious illness or require a major operation. Your own Veterinary Surgeon will be able to recommend a reliable company, and a policy that is suited to your needs. However, it should be noted that these policies do not cover routine treatment such as neutering or vaccination.

The various animal welfare organisations (RSPCA, PDSA, Blue Cross, and so on) have branches in nearly all areas today and do great work in caring for the pets of people who are unable to afford a visit to a private Veterinary Surgeon. A cat should never be allowed to suffer because of financial problems. The Yellow Pages or the telephone directory will almost certainly give the address of some organisation that is willing to help in genuine cases of need.

Proper care

Although cats are remarkably trouble-free pets, the care of any living thing involves some responsibility.

It is not necessary to buy a licence for a cat (which is perhaps a pity) and indeed cats hardly exist at all in the eyes of the law, except in relation to the rabies regulations and in the sense that they are protected by the Prevention of Cruelty to Animals Act. Unfortunately, it is rather easy to acquire a kitten and often thoughtless people take home an attractive fluffy pet only to abandon it later if it becomes a nuisance. Before becoming an owner consider the responsibilities you are taking on and be certain that your new cat will be properly cared for, especially at holiday times when you may have to go away.

SKELETON OF THE CAT
(and descriptions of the bones)

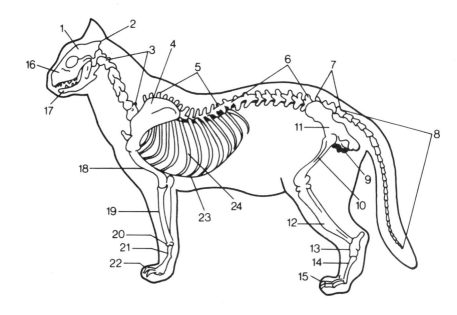

(1)	Cranium (top of skull)	(13)	Tarsus (ankle)
(2)	Occiput (back of skull)	(14)	Metatarsus (rear paw)
(3)	Cervical vertebrae (neck)	(15)	Phalanges (toes)
(4)	Scapula (shoulder blade)	(16)	Nasal bones
(5)	Thoracic vertebrae (spinal column)	(17)	Mandible (lower jaw)
(6)	Lumbar vertebrae (spinal column)	(18)	Humerus (upper arm bone)
(7)	Sacral vertebrae	(19)	Radius and Ulna (lower arm bones)
(8)	Coccygeal vertebrae (tail)	(20)	Carpus (wrist)
(9)	Pubis (lower pelvis)	(21)	Metacarpus (front paw)
(10)	Femur (thigh)	(22)	Phalanges (toes)
(11)	Pelvis (hindquarters)	(23)	Sternum (breast bone)
(12)	Tibia and Fibula (lower rear leg bones)	(24)	Rib cage

Population

There is a population explosion in the cat (as well as the human) world at present, which means that neutering really is important if we are to ensure that the numbers of cats are to be limited to those for which caring homes can be found. It is sad that even in the Western World, where we consider that we care for the welfare of animals, each town has its colony of homeless and unwanted strays.

It has been estimated that a bitch could produce 4,400 offspring in a period of seven years. Female cats breed even more frequently so the possible number of descendants of an unneutered queen in her own lifetime is staggering (and, of course, the males must take some of the credit or blame for the number as well).

Which breed?

There is, today, an absolute abundance of different breeds of cat to choose from, although probably the Siamese and Persian remain top pure breed favourites. Each has its own particular attraction, and breeding or showing pedigree cats can provide an interesting hobby. However, praising purebred cats should not make us overlook the ordinary English crossbreeds. They come in a huge variety of coat colour and length, and each one has its own particular charm.

Longevity

Cats today, just like people, are living longer as a result of better feeding and better care and through the introduction of antibiotics and other modern drugs that help to combat the diseases that used to shorten their lives. The record for longevity is held by a cat called Puss, from Cullompton in Devon, who died in 1939 a day after his 36th birthday. However, many household pets reach the age of sixteen or seventeen. In other words the small financial outlay in buying and caring for a cat should be well repaid. If you look after your cat well he could be with you for a long time to come.

VARIETIES OF CATS

Cats are divided into two main classes - long-haired and short-haired.

Within these groups are many varieties, too numerous to list with new varieties being added all the time.

If you are interested in obtaining detailed descriptions of the types then a guide may be purchased from the Governing Council of the Cat Fancy (the address can be found under "Useful Contacts" at the end of this book).

CHAPTER 2

WHEN YOUR CAT HAS KITTENS

Cats usually make good mothers and seem to enjoy maternity. Supervising the rearing of a litter of kittens contributes a lot of pleasure to most households, especially where there are children, who really love to watch the progress of the new arrivals. It is especially pleasant, if circumstances allow, to keep at least one kitten as an addition to the family since it provides companionship for the mother and is always valued and spoiled as the baby. However, if you cannot cope with a larger family of cats, or expect to find difficulty in rehoming kittens, it is much kinder to have your cat neutered as soon as possible, and avoid the problem before it happens.

GOOD HOMES ARE ESSENTIAL

Before deciding to let your cat have kittens do try to be certain that you can find sufficient good homes for the new family. It is much kinder to have your cat neutered as soon as she is old enough rather than having the upsetting problem of unwanted kittens.

SHOULD YOU LET YOUR CAT BREED?

There is no evidence at all to support the idea that it is better for cat's health to let her have at least one litter of kittens. The neutered female is probably on average longer living, requires less medical care, and makes an ideal family pet.

THE BREEDING SEASON - OESTRUS OR CALLING

Female cats tend to come into season (or "calling" as it is known) from about six months old and they will, if allowed, become pregnant at this age, which of course is too young for their own welfare, since they are not fully grown and mature until nine months to one year.

There are two main breeding periods; the beginning of January to the end of May, and the beginning of July to the end of August. Cats come into season less during the main winter months when the daylight hours are shorter but otherwise the times are rather variable and cannot be relied upon.

During the breeding period, cats tend to come into season for one to three days at a time, at intervals of fourteen to twenty-one days, but occasionally the season may last as long as ten days. This makes it particularly difficult to ensure that if kittens are not wanted, the cat is kept in for the appropriate time.

BEHAVIOUR IN SEASON

Behaviour

Cats really do call when in oestrus. They develop a persistent and raucous voice, quite unlike their normal miaow and this is particularly noticeable in the Siamese. They become very restless and try to get out of the house at any opportunity and often at this time you will find that one or more unneutered tom cats have taken up residence in the back garden. There is also a tendency for the females to roll about on their backs, giving the impression to inexperienced cat owners that they are in some acute pain.

PREVENTING SEASON

Family planning

The nuisance of the season problem can be reduced by means of an injection or tablets to prevent the season (see Chapter 3) but this is mainly of value to breeders who wish to postpone kittens until the cat is mature. For most households neutering is the most satisfactory measure.

Mating tends to be rather unintentional or unpremeditated in most cases for the family pet cat. If your cat gets out during the oestrus period she will almost certainly be mated and since ovulation appears to occur as a response to mating, the chances of conception are very high.

Under urban conditions, where a female cat is often kept in because of traffic risk, it may be slightly more difficult if kittens are wanted. In this case it is probably best to consult with the owner of a pedigree male cat who may be willing to arrange a mating (see Chapter 4, section on breeding and showing), or may know of someone who owns a crossbred unneutered male.

Usually if a cat has been mated, the symptoms of oestrus subside within 24 hours and do not recur until about five to six weeks after the birth of the kittens. Cats are less likely to conceive whilst they are feeding their kittens but this is not, by any means, a reliable rule.

PREGNANCY

Gestation

Pregnancy usually lasts for 63 to 65 days but, of course, except in the case of pedigree cats, the exact date of mating is often uncertain (see table to calculate time).

RECOGNITION

Recognition of pregnancy

4 - 5 weeks - your Veterinary Surgeon will be able to determine, as a rule, if your cat is in kitten by feeling the abdomen to detect the presence of the hard spherical foetuses (rather like marbles at this stage). Ultra Sonography may also be used to diagnose pregnancy.

5 - 6 weeks - abdominal swelling may be noticed and there will be some enlargement of the milk glands.

8 - 9 weeks - the movement of the kittens may be noticed when the mother cat is relaxed.

However, it often happens that all these signs are missed or mistaken for a weight problem, and the first indication of pregnancy is the sound of kittens coming from the airing cupboard or some other unsuitable spot. This is even more surprising to owners who were certain that their cat was a tom!

A SUITABLE BED

Kittening

It is important to accustom your cat to sleeping in a special place that you have selected for the kittening at least one week before the kittens are due, or she may make her own plans to occupy the spare bed. If she is disturbed, or if for any reason she feels that the litter is in danger, a mother cat will sometimes transport her family for considerable distances, carrying each one in turn by the scruff of the neck.

Pregnancy table

Served January	Due to kitten March	Served February	Due to kitten April	Served March	Due to kitten May	Served April	Due to kitten June	Served May	Due to kitten July	Served June	Due to kitten August	Served July	Due to kitten September	Served August	Due to kitten October	Served September	Due to kitten November	Served October	Due to kitten December	Served November	Due to kitten January	Served December	Due to kitten February
1	5	1	5	1	3	1	3	1	3	1	3	1	2	1	3	1	3	1	3	1	3	1	2
2	6	2	6	2	4	2	4	2	4	2	4	2	3	2	4	2	4	2	4	2	4	2	3
3	7	3	7	3	5	3	5	3	5	3	5	3	4	3	5	3	5	3	5	3	5	3	4
4	8	4	8	4	6	4	6	4	6	4	6	4	5	4	6	4	6	4	6	4	6	4	5
5	9	5	9	5	7	5	7	5	7	5	7	5	6	5	7	5	7	5	7	5	7	5	6
6	10	6	10	6	8	6	8	6	8	6	8	6	7	6	8	6	8	6	8	6	8	6	7
7	11	7	11	7	9	7	9	7	9	7	9	7	8	7	9	7	9	7	9	7	9	7	8
8	12	8	12	8	10	8	10	8	10	8	10	8	9	8	10	8	10	8	10	8	10	8	9
9	13	9	13	9	11	9	11	9	11	9	11	9	10	9	11	9	11	9	11	9	11	9	10
10	14	10	14	10	12	10	12	10	12	10	12	10	11	10	12	10	12	10	12	10	12	10	11
11	15	11	15	11	13	11	13	11	13	11	13	11	12	11	13	11	13	11	13	11	13	11	12
12	16	12	16	12	14	12	14	12	14	12	14	12	13	12	14	12	14	12	14	12	14	12	13
13	17	13	17	13	15	13	15	13	15	13	15	13	14	13	15	13	15	13	15	13	15	13	14
14	18	14	18	14	16	14	16	14	16	14	16	14	15	14	16	14	16	14	16	14	16	14	15
15	19	15	19	15	17	15	17	15	17	15	17	15	16	15	17	15	17	15	17	15	17	15	16
16	20	16	20	16	18	16	18	16	18	16	18	16	17	16	18	16	18	16	18	16	18	16	17
17	21	17	21	17	19	17	19	17	19	17	19	17	18	17	19	17	19	17	19	17	19	17	18
18	22	18	22	18	20	18	20	18	20	18	20	18	19	18	20	18	20	18	20	18	20	18	19
19	23	19	23	19	21	19	21	19	21	19	21	19	20	19	21	19	21	19	21	19	21	19	20
20	24	20	24	20	22	20	22	20	22	20	22	20	21	20	22	20	22	20	22	20	22	20	21
21	25	21	25	21	23	21	23	21	23	21	23	21	22	21	23	21	23	21	23	21	23	21	22
22	26	22	26	22	24	22	24	22	24	22	24	22	23	22	24	22	24	22	24	22	24	22	23
23	27	23	27	23	25	23	25	23	25	23	25	23	24	23	25	23	25	23	25	23	25	23	24
24	28	24	28	24	26	24	26	24	26	24	26	24	25	24	26	24	26	24	26	24	26	24	25
25	29	25	29	25	27	25	27	25	27	25	27	25	26	25	27	25	27	25	27	25	27	25	26
26	30	26	30	26	28	26	28	26	28	26	28	26	27	26	28	26	28	26	28	26	28	26	27
27	31	27	May 1	27	29	27	29	27	29	27	29	27	28	27	29	27	29	27	29	27	29	27	28
28	Apr 1	28	2	28	30	28	30	28	30	28	30	28	29	28	30	28	30	28	30	28	30	28	Mar 1
29	2	29	3	29	31	29	July 1	29	31	29	31	29	30	29	31	29	Dec 1	29	31	29	31	29	2
30	3			30	June 1	30	2	30	Aug 1	30	Sept 1	30	Oct 1	30	Nov 1	30	2	30	Jan 1	30	Feb 1	30	3
31	4			31	2			31	2			31	2	31	2			31	2			31	4

A strong cardboard box is the best choice for a bed. Choose one that is large enough to accommodate the mother and her kittens comfortably and leave high sides, or a lid, to allow a sense of security and privacy. A step of several inches high should be left at the entrance side to prevent any adventurous tiny kittens wandering off into danger.

Keeping clean

Line the box with several layers of newspaper. Providing that the room itself is comfortably warm this will provide sufficient bedding during the birth and early days. Newspaper has the advantage that it can be removed in layers if necessary and burnt as it becomes soiled. It is less dangerous than blankets, which may become wrapped around the young kittens causing suffocation. Artificial sheepskin bedding that is machine washable is also an acceptable alternative.

Place the box in the quietest and most secluded area of the room. Mother cats much prefer to be left undisturbed in the early days to care for their family.

FEEDING DURING PREGNANCY

1. Up to six weeks

If your cat is receiving a sensible balanced diet it is not usually necessary to increase the volume of food during the first five to six weeks (see Chapter 4).

VITAMIN & MINERAL SUPPLEMENTS

Correct diet

If your cat is on a commercially prepared diet little supplementation should be required. Pet food manufacturers go to considerable lengths to ensure that the diet is balanced and contains all the vitamins and minerals that are required.

Supple-mentation

However, if your cat is a fussy eater, to ensure that she is getting her daily requirements, a multi-vitamin/mineral supplement can be added to the diet (e.g. Sherley's Vionate).

2. From six to nine weeks

At this stage the cat will probably develop a large appetite and the food can, if required, be increased gradually to twice the normal quantity. It should preferably be divided into three or four meals to avoid abdominal discomfort.

EXERCISE

Tone

There is no need to place any special restrictions on the movements of the mother cat during pregnancy. In the earlier stages her usual activities will help to maintain muscle tone and in the later stages the weight of the kittens will probably slow her down quite sufficiently.

Care should be taken when picking her up to see that she is supported under the abdomen, to avoid any risk of twisting the uterus (or womb) in the later stages of pregnancy.

THE BIRTH

The process of birth is usually divided into three stages and, as a rule, mother cats will accomplish all these without any outside aid. However, occasionally difficulties may arise, so it is as well just to peep into the box from time to time to be sure that all is proceeding according to plan (see later in chapter for possible complications).

First stage of labour (6-12 hours)

When the birth is about to take place the cat will probably wander about and seem uneasy. She will often go in and out of the basket, sometimes "treading" the bedding, and making a loud purring sound. There may be a slight vaginal discharge and body temperature at the time drops to below 100° F (37-8°C).

Second stage (3-12 hours)

There is a definite straining and the cat may cry out, especially with the first litter. Usually after about thirty minutes the first kitten will appear at the vulva and will be expelled quite quickly. Sometimes the kitten will remain enveloped within the foetal membranes in a transparent sac but, as a rule, the mother will break this at once and will start to lick and wash her kitten very vigorously to clean it and stimulate breathing. She will then bite through the umbilical cord and in a surprisingly short time the kitten will start to cry and then make its way round to the milk glands, settling down contentedly to feed.

HEAD OR BREECH

Kittens may arrive normally by either the head or breech (tail and hind feet) presentation. However, in the case of a breech there is more risk of suffocation if the birth should be delayed.

Third stage

The third stage is the expulsion of the afterbirth or placenta (the foetal membrane which connected the kitten to the blood supply of the mother by means of the umbilical cord). In most cases the kitten will be expelled still attached to the afterbirth and the mother will bite at the cord to sever it then eat the membranes. This looks rather unpleasant but it is just how a cat would have behaved while living in the wild. It has been suggested that the afterbirth of the cat and the dog may contain hormones which are of value in the production of milk, or that they may have served as a source of protein in the first 48 hours after birth when the mother was reluctant to leave her young. However, if too many are eaten they will probably cause vomiting and with a large litter it may be wise to remove any placentas that are seen and dispose of them.

Sometimes, since the cat birth is a multiple process, stages two and three may tend to overlap, so that two or more kittens may be born followed after an interval by the appropriate afterbirths. However, if any afterbirths are retained they can cause infection and serious illness, so if you feel uncertain as to whether or not this stage has been completed, or if your cat seems uneasy or unwell, consult a Veterinary Surgeon.

Tying and cutting the umbilical cord

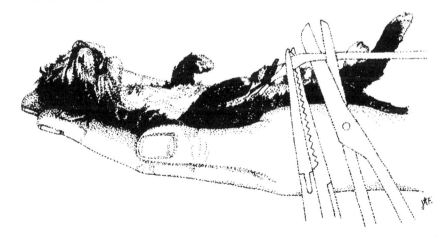

Cutting the cord

It is rarely necessary to cut the cord since the mother does this job herself. However, if after a period of about ten minutes she has not done so and it becomes necessary, remember that hygiene is extremely important. Scrub your hands with a disinfectant solution and apply a tight ligature (using boiled sewing thread) to the cord, about two inches away from the kitten's abdomen. Using a pair of scissors sterilised by boiling, cut through the cord on the side away from the knot. The cord will shrivel and can be trimmed off later if necessary.

The number of kittens is usually from three to seven (the average is four).

The interval between births varies from ten to sixty minutes, though even longer delays may be quite normal if the cat is not straining hard or showing any signs of distress.

New-born kittens

Usually, once a litter is complete, the mother will wash all her family and settle down to sleep. She will not, as a rule, take any food or drink during the birth but when it is over she will probably appreciate a drink of milk if it is offered to her in the bed. Some cats will refuse to leave their kittens at all during the first day, even for food. However, if possible they should be lifted out to relieve themselves, so that bedding can be changed and the kittens checked for health.

PROBLEMS

When to call the vet

Although kittening is usually easy and free from problems, troubles can occur and consulting a Veterinary Surgeon in good time may well save a life.

If your cat has not managed to give birth after straining for more than half an hour, it is possible that there is a wrongly positioned kitten. This usually means that instead of lying in a streamlined "head first" or "tail and hind feet first" position, the kitten is lying transversely across the neck of the uterus (or womb). This condition, if not corrected, will be fatal, so get advice quickly.

Caesarean section

In cases where a cat is unable to produce her kitten because of wrong positioning, oversize, or other conditions, an operation (caesarean section) is usually required. If it is carried out in good time, before the mother has become exhausted, the chances that she will recover and be able to rear her kittens are good.

The operation requires a general anaesthetic. The kittens are removed through a surgical wound in the middle of the abdomen or on the flank, which is then closed with nylon stitches (removed normally after seven to ten days). The Veterinary Surgeon may recommend sterilisation (neutering) at the same time, depending on the individual circumstances.

The cat will require warmth and careful nursing (see Chapter 6 for advice on care and feeding) but unless there are complications which endanger the life of the mother cat she can be given her kittens immediately on recovery from the anaesthetic. They usually provide a considerable boost to her morale and will to live.

Large kittens

If a particulary large kitten has been partly expelled and then becomes wedged, it will usually be necessary to get Veterinary assistance. However, in an emergency, the owner may be able to help, providing that the kitten is lying in a normal position. Check carefully that either the head and both front legs are visible, or both hind feet and tail. Grasp the kitten with a clean dry towel and as the cat strains pull gently but firmly in a downward direction. Twisting the kitten very gently into a diagonal position may also help. The pelvis are oval-shaped, and so wider at the diagonal. If any doubt at all is felt about the position of the kitten, it should not be touched. A Veterinary Surgeon should be consulted as soon as possible.

Afterbirth

If you suspect that your cat has not expelled all the kittens or the afterbirths, if she seems listless and unwilling to eat or care for the kittens, if there is an excessive or unpleasant discharge from the vagina, or if she is running a temperature (see Chapter 8 for how to take a temperature), consult a Veterinary Surgeon at once. Antibiotic treatment may be needed to prevent the onset of a highly fatal septicaemia.

Mastitis

Hardness and swelling or discolouration of the milk glands may indicate mastitis. This will not only make the mother cat ill but will prevent her from feeding the kittens, so get advice quickly.

Prolapsed uterus

Fortunately, a prolapsed uterus is fairly uncommon. The mother cat continues straining after the kittens are born and the uterus is expelled, which appears as a bloodstained spongy mass under the tail. This condition is extremely serious. Keep the patient in a clean warm spot (for instance on a clean cloth in a basket) and contact a Veterinary Surgeon as soon as possible.

REVIVING KITTENS

Sometimes after a delayed or difficult birth a kitten may appear to be dead, but if a heartbeat can be detected it is well worth attempting revival. Holding the kitten with the head slightly lower than the feet to allow any fluid to escape from the lungs, rub and massage the body gently with a warm dry towel. At intervals open the mouth (making sure that the tongue is depressed and not sticking to the roof of the mouth) and blow gently into the mouth, taking care not to touch the kitten with your own mouth, to inflate the lungs and stimulate breathing. If any signs of life are seen, continue until breathing becomes regular, then as soon as possible return the kitten to its mother.

ABNORMALITIES

Abnormal kittens

Before attempting to revive an apparently lifeless kitten, check that it is not suffering from any congenital abnormality. These may vary from kittens that are born with the muscular wall of the abdomen totally absent, to the less obvious but equally serious cleft palate which prevents the young animal from sucking and feeding. If kittens are born alive with any of these defects they should be taken to a Veterinary Surgeon as soon as possible to be humanely destroyed.

Remember, of course, that all kittens are born with their eyes closed and do not start to open them until they are about twelve days old.

THE NEW KITTENS

Sexing

Determining the sex of very young kittens is not easy but it may be of some consequence in deciding which kittens can be reared for potential homes. Your Veterinary Surgeon will certainly be able to help you if you have occasion to consult him, but otherwise you may be able to come to the right conclusion after reading the description in Chapter 3.

CARING FOR THE MOTHER CAT & HER KITTENS

During the first three to four weeks of their lives the mother cat will care for her kittens completely. She will not only feed them but also keep them scrupulously clean and by her constant licking ensure that bladder and bowels are functioning properly.

Feeding the mother

To supply the kittens' needs, without losing bodily condition, the food requirements of the mother cat are very high and she can be fed almost at will. At least three high-protein meals (see Chapter 4 on Feeding) daily should be offered in addition to milk or Lactol. Fresh water should be available at all times as a high fluid intake is necessary to maintain the supply of milk for the family.

WEANING

To avoid excessive strain on the mother, especially in the case of a large litter, it is advisable to start weaning the kittens from about four weeks of age.

First foods

To tempt the kittens to try solid food offer interesting flavours. Well-stewed or shredded rabbit and chicken are usually popular, or shredded minced meat, boiled fish and well mashed canned meat or fish. Once the kittens have learned to lap, milk or Lactol should be offered three times daily.

Patience will be needed at first to persuade the kittens to feed. The food is best placed on a large flat plate. Try to ensure that each kitten gets a fair share and increase the amount gradually until by the age of five weeks you should be giving three to four meals daily (each kitten taking about 3 ounces (85 g) of solid food in addition to milk). By seven to eight weeks old, the kittens should be independent of their mother and she will probably have started to get tired of her demanding family. It is best to provide an extra sleeping box on a higher level where she can retreat from time to time.

Season

Remember that at five to six weeks after the birth of the kittens the mother is likely to come into season, so she must be carefully watched if another litter of kittens is not to follow too soon.

CARING FOR ORPHAN KITTENS

To rear a large litter of orphan kittens is almost impossibly demanding for the average household. If the situation occurs every attempt should be made to find a foster mother. However, in the case of just one to two kittens success is possible if the time can be sacrificed to give at least two weeks of constant care. The task can be a very rewarding one; since orphan kittens often grow up to be very strong healthy cats.

Warmth

Warmth is of the greatest importance - a room temperature of about 70°F (21°C) is ideal. The box in which the kittens are kept should be placed close to a constant source of heat such as a radiator or boiler. A well-wrapped hot-water bottle should be placed in the box for the kittens to snuggle up to as a substitute mother.
The box should have high sides since tiny kittens are surprisingly active and adventurous. It should be lined with a thick layer of newspaper and on the top of this a layer of blanket or old quilt for warmth.

Hygiene

To substitute for the constant licking action of the mother cat, the orphan kittens should be wiped all over after each meal with a warm damp flannel then thoroughly dried.

Health care

Constipation can usually be corrected by the addition of a Veterinary preparation to the milk mixture.

Diarrhoea is more serious and a Veterinary Surgeon should be consulted since dehydration (loss of body fluids) can very rapidly cause the death of young animals.

FEEDING

Lactol

Cow's milk is not sufficiently rich in protein to act as a substitute for the mother's milk. Lactol is a complete milk food formulated to act as a replacement or supplement to the mother's milk.

Admin-istration

Lactol can be given with either an eye dropper or a Lactol Feeding Bottle but young kittens, even though hungry, are often reluctant to attempt to feed and endless patience will be needed. The Lactol mixture should be given at approximately blood heat (101°F/38.3°C). Follow the mixing instructions on the Lactol tin.

First two weeks - feed every two hours

Second two weeks - feed every four hours

Then every six hours

How much?

Quantities will vary, but the kittens can be allowed as much as they are willing to take at each feed.

As a measure of progress, a healthy kitten should gain about one third of an ounce (9 g) in weight daily and should double its birth weight in eight to nine days (kittens can be weighed using kitchen scales).

Solid foods

From two weeks of age, the kitten may be offered Lactol from a shallow bowl. Solid foods can be introduced from three to four weeks. Stewed meat or fish, finely shredded and mixed with gravy, and sieved meat or fish baby foods are ideal. The latter have the advantage that they can be given with a spoon as an introduction to new foods. Once the kitten has learned to lap, the task of feeding becomes much easier. Lactol can be continued in the diet and management can proceed as for the normal kitten.

The Lactol Feeding Bottle

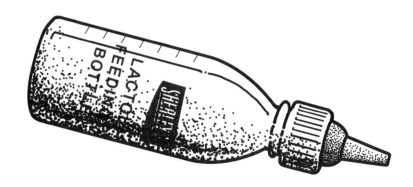

TOILET TRAINING

As soon as the kittens start to leave their mother they should be placed on the litter tray after every feed to start early house training. A clean kitten will be a particularly welcome arrival in its new home.

KITTEN HEALTH

Worming

Roundworms can constitute a danger to young kittens and even if the mother has been dosed, it is essential to treat the kittens as well. Modern treatments such as Sherley's Worming Cream or Worming Syrup are safe and palatable and do not require pre-fasting. Mother and kittens should be wormed from two weeks after the birth.

See Chapter 5 - Internal and External Parasites

BEFORE YOUR KITTEN LEAVES HOME

Fleas & mites

Check for fleas and ear mites. Give your kitten a thorough overhaul for parasites before sending it to a new home (see Chapter 5 - Internal and External Parasites).

VACCINATION & NEUTERING

Stress to the new owners the importance of having kittens neutered and of vaccination against viral diseases - see Chapter 3 - since the importance of preventative medicine does not always occur to the new cat owner. Your Veterinary Surgeon may supply a leaflet on the subject.

It will also help if you give details of the type of food that you have used.

All these things will help to make your cat welcome in his new home and will ensure that he settles down happily with his new owners.

CARING FOR YOUR NEW KITTEN

CHOOSING A KITTEN

It is probably true to say that, whilst acquiring a puppy is usually a deliberate choice, choosing (or being chosen by) a cat is often accidental. Sometimes a homeless kitten arrives in the garden, or a neighbour is anxious to find homes for an unplanned litter, or one hears that a kitten will be put to sleep unless a home is found at once. Almost without premeditation one becomes a cat owner. However, it is important to check first that the whole family agrees to the new arrival. It is not fair through an impulse of generosity to bring a kitten into a house where it is not really welcome. To provide a home is not enough. A lot of love and care will be needed as well.

THE RIGHT AGE

Eight
weeks old

Ideally kittens should be eight weeks old before they are sent to a new home, or if younger, they should be completely weaned and used to sleeping away from the mother cat. A kitten of four to five weeks old which has not learned to lap or take sufficient solid food on its own, has a very poor chance of survival in the outside world. However, the arrival of a kitten is not always premeditated or arranged. If your new pet looks much younger and smaller than you had expected it will need special care in the first few days if it is to develop into a healthy young cat.

WHERE TO GET YOUR KITTEN

A home you know

The healthiest kittens are, as a rule, those that come from good private homes. They have had the advantage of proper feeding during their first weeks of life, and a relatively low risk of contact with outside infections. Even more important, a kitten from a kind and loving home that is used to being handled by people is more likely to have an even temperament and be free from excessive nervousness. It should be easier to feed (especially if you check with the owner as to previous types and times of feeding), and it may even be house-trained, at least to some extent.

If you do not know of any kittens in your immediate circle, try asking at your local corner shop, where this kind of information may often be found. Alternatively, look in your local or evening paper. Kittens are often advertised as "free to good homes".

Cats' Homes

It is certainly an act of kindness to give a home to a kitten from a Cats' Home but this is not always a venture with a happy ending. Young kittens which have been handed into a shelter at five or six weeks of age have very little resistance and in this situation there is every chance that they will come into contact with infection (most commonly the flu or enteritis viruses). A kitten that appears quite healthy to you, or to the home official who hands it out, may well be in the incubating stages of disease. The recovery rate for very young kittens is not good. For your new pet to die within a week or two can be a most upsetting experience for children in the family - and for adults too.

Pet shops

Likewise, care is also needed when buying a kitten from a pet shop. Make sure that the shop has a good source of kittens and a high standard of hygiene. The kitten you choose should be lively and healthy.

PEDIGREE CATS

Breeders

When buying a pedigree cat the same rules apply. A long pedigree and a high price are no guarantee of good health, so wherever possible collect your kitten directly from the breeder and find out as much as possible about its background. A reliable breeder will, as a rule, agree to let your own Veterinary Surgeon examine the kitten for health before you complete the purchase. It is in the best interests of breeders' reputations to sell only sound kittens and they are usually glad to know that the animals that they have reared are going to caring homes.

BUYER BEWARE

Never, on any account, buy a kitten unseen from an advertisement. A young animal that is sent by train may easily suffer as a result of unexpected and even unavoidable delays. Even if it is sold under a "money back if not satisfactory" agreement, you may be involved in considerable trouble or even heartbreak if your new pet does not match up to the advertisement.

Choosing your cat

There are, nowadays, a great number of pedigree cats to choose from, although Siamese in their various varieties are probably top favourites. These cats have been carefully selected and bred and their price will vary with their rarity and their show potential. For the cat lover, breeding and showing can provide an interesting hobby. The best way to learn about cats and to choose your favourite kind is to visit your local cat show (see Chapter 4). However, unless you really have a lot of time to spare avoid the long-haired Persian varieties. The enchanting pretty fluffy kittens, which are so often featured in advertisements, are only kept in this way by constant care, and a neglected and tangled Persian becomes a misery to itself.

PEDIGREE CROSS KITTENS

Half-breed

Half-bred pedigree kittens (usually the result of the accidental mating of a Siamese or other type of pedigree cat) are sometimes offered for sale or free to good homes. While they do not, as a rule, follow the colour of the pedigree, they do have many of the breed characteristics, and make very attractive pets.

CROSS-BREDS

While the various pedigree cats are very attractive, they have no monopoly of charm and intelligence. Whether your crossbred cat is handsome, pretty, or just unusual, it is fairly certain that you will think that it is the best in the world.

MALE OR FEMALE

The sex of the new kitten is not of great consequence if it is to be a family pet, since most thoughtful owners will probably decide on neutering in either case (see section on neutering later in this chapter). The temperaments and characters of the neutered male and female are very similar. The female may, marginally, be sweeter and more affectionate and marginally, the male may be more independent, but these are only generalisations and many owners would probably disagree.

Male or
female?

It is not easy for the average person to distinguish the sex of a very young kitten. In fact, many kittens are booked in for neutering under the wrong sex, to the great surprise of the owner who was certain that their "female" was a "tom" or vice versa.

SEX LINKED COLOURS

Colours

In some cases the sex can be surmised from its colour. True tortoiseshells are always females, but doubt sometimes arises as to the identification of this colour - a particular mixture of reddish brown and black hairs.

Ginger cats are often, but not always, males. Contrary to popular opinion, ginger females are not sterile and can breed successfully.

White cats

However, it is true that in some cases an all white colour in cats is linked with deafness. This can be a great disadvantage since a deaf cat is exposed to dangers - both from traffic and animal enemies.

IDENTIFICATION

To attempt to identify the sex of your new kitten, first stand "it" on a table in a good light and lift up the tail.

In the male the uro-genital opening is a small circular dot below and slightly separated from the anus, rather like a colon (:). It may also be possible to see the slight swelling of the testicles, just below the anus.

In the female the opening (vulva) is in the same situation, below but closer to the anus and is rather more elongated vertically, like an inverted exclamation mark (see diagram). When looking at a male and female kitten together the differences are fairly obvious but considering one on its own can be puzzling, especially when they are very young.

Sexing kittens: the female is on the left and the male is on the right

WHETHER PEDIGREE OR CROSS-BRED - A HEALTHY KITTEN IS THE IMPORTANT CHOICE

A litter of young kittens is a very attractive sight and to most prospective cat owners the temptation is strong to choose the one that looks the prettiest and take it home at once. However, a little time spent on checking over the proposed new addition to the family may save some trouble and worry in the weeks to come.

GENERAL APPEARANCE

A healthy kitten should be bright, active, and interested in the world around it. One that is very shy, or inclined to back into a corner and spit at strangers may have a difficult temperament and grow up to be a problem cat.

Bright and active

Plumpness is a healthy sign but an over-distended stomach in proportion to the body may indicate poor feeding, or the presence of roundworms (see Chapter 5).

The coat should be shiny, clean, and free from parasites, although even in the best of homes the occasional flea may be found. However, this is not a serious problem and it is a good precaution to give any new kitten a once-over with a flea comb on arrival in the new home (see Chapter 5 - Internal & External Parasites).

Ears

The ears should be examined for the hard crusty deposits in the ear canal, which may indicate the presence of ear mites (see Chapter 5 - Internal and External Parasites). This condition can certainly be cured by the application of suitable drops from your Veterinary Surgeon, but a severe infestation can make a young kitten quite ill and it is probably best to ask the owner to carry out treatment before taking the kitten home.

The healthy kitten has clear bright eyes and an only slightly moist nose.

Eyes and nose

Beware of the so-called "cold". Cats do not get the trivial common cold as humans do and any sneezing or discharge from the eyes or nose must be taken as a danger signal. It may be a symptom of the onset of cat flu (see Chapter 7), a viral disease which can be very serious and fatal, or it may indicate that the kitten has chronic catarrh, a condition which, whilst it rarely kills, can be a recurring nuisance throughout life. In some areas, especially farms, this condition may be found in nearly all the cats, which have continuously runny eyes and noses, together with sneezing and catarrhal symptoms. They are often permanently stunted as a result.

Having said all this, it is a fact that many cats arrive unexpectedly in the home, sometimes in poor condition as a result of straying and exposure. Check through all the previous points and also consider whether there is any sign of diarrhoea, or if the kitten seems unable to take food. Young animals have very little resistance to infection and, if they are unable to feed, quickly become dehydrated and weak. In these circumstances it is important to take the kitten to your own Veterinary Surgeon as soon as possible for examination and treatment.

BRINGING HOME THE NEW KITTEN

Cat box

When collecting your new kitten remember that he, or she, may well be frightened by the first contact with the noisy outside world. Nervous kittens are inclined to bolt, so it is important to take a strong carrying box of some kind. If you have a proper cat box this is, of course, ideal.

An emergency cat box made by fitting a large box over a smaller box

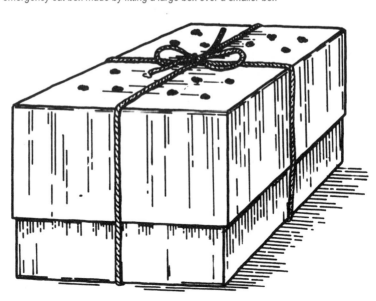

Cardboard

If you decide to buy a cat box, it will certainly be of use in the future if your cat has to travel, or even for necessary visits to the vet (see Chapter 4 - Caring for the Adult Cat, for more information on this subject). If you do not want to go to this expense you will probably find that your local animal welfare society (RSPCA or PDSA) or a Veterinary Surgeon sells strong cardboard cat carriers quite cheaply. They are very suitable for transporting kittens, though they may not be adequate for a boisterous adult cat.

As an emergency cat box, two strong cardboard boxes can be used (after making ventilation holes), the large fitting completely over the smaller to form a lid and being tied around with string (see diagram). This may seem an unnecessary amount of caution but nothing could be sadder than to lose a young kitten in a strange area through lack of taking care.

Finally, a warm blanket in the box will be comforting, especially if the weather is cold.

COLLAR & NAME TAG

Cat collar

It is a good idea to buy a proper cat collar (with an elasticated safety section or quick-release buckle to avoid the risk of strangulation if he should become entangled in a tree) as soon as you get your new kitten and to have a disc made with your name, address, and telephone number on. It is only too easy for young animals to stray and your chances of recovering your pet will be much greater if he can be easily identified. For kittens over 6 months of age a Sherley's Lost & Found Flea Collar can be used. Each individual Lost & Found Collar has its own unique identification number printed on it, and this information is registered with Sherley's on a central database. If your kitten should become lost, the finder can ring the Freephone number that is also printed on the collar, and Sherley's can help reunite you with your pet. An alternative is to have your cat microchipped. Each chip is unique, it can be read by a vet, animal warden, or a number of animal charities. Your details are kept on a central computer, so that you can be contacted if your cat is found. The microchip is small, and it is inserted under the skin by your vet, or other trained individual. Many Siamese cats learn to walk on a collar and lead like dogs. This idea could quite usefully be applied to other breeds, giving a little more mobility and safety to strange situations such as when travelling.

THE NEW HOME

Taking care

Cats are inquisitive animals and your new kitten will certainly want to get out of the basket and make a thorough inspection of his new surroundings, so make certain that all doors and windows are shut. Also, if there is an open fire or fire grate, make certain that there is a guard in place because timid kittens have been known to bolt up chimneys. It is really best to confine the newcomer at first to one room as far as possible, until he has become accustomed to the place. He will probably not be house-trained and this will minimise the risk of accidents occurring on carpets. It is also for his own safety, since tiny kittens can so easily be stepped on and injured when they are encountered unexpectedly.

FREEDOM OR SAFETY - WHEN TO LET YOUR NEW KITTEN OUT

This is always a very difficult decision to take and depends upon the individual circumstances. At least one week should be allowed for the kitten to adapt to his surroundings and for the sights, sounds and smells which make up the new home to become imprinted on his mind. If you have a well-enclosed garden you may then decide to let him out for a stroll and an investigation, but only under supervision, and preferably just before a meal (this ensures he will come back!).

TRAFFIC DANGERS

Traffic

If you live near a busy road you may have to decide to keep your cat in altogether. Unfortunately, there is no way of preventing a cat from straying into danger. If you allow your cat to go out alone in an area where there is heavy traffic, you must face the fact that he may one day be injured or killed.

GOING OUT AT NIGHT

Cats in the wild are probably, at least partly, nocturnal animals and on summer nights they love to stay out chasing moths and other bigger game. However, the danger from traffic at night is even greater than by day, since cats are often injured after being dazzled by car headlights and there is always the thought that a pet may be lying hurt for some hours before he is found. Under today's conditions it is probably kinder and wiser to keep cats in unless you live in a very rural area.

Partial
freedom

As a compromise, it is worth considering constructing a wire netting enclosure in the garden for your kitten. If it is furnished with an old tree branch as a seat and a place to scratch the claws, it will provide a little fresh air and exercise together with peace of mind for the owner. The cat run need not be large but it should be strongly made. Choose an area that has some shade as well as sunshine and provide a box or shelter to give protection from rain if your cat is to be left for some hours at a time.

BUTTERING THE PAWS

There was an old superstition that buttering the paws prevented a new kitten from straying away. There is certainly no basis in fact for this at all but people thought that a cat that was cleaning the butter off his feet would be too busy to stray.

MEETING THE CHILDREN

Introduction

Children usually love kittens and kittens thoroughly enjoy being played with and encouraged to chase a piece of paper or string. However, it is important to teach children that pets are not just toys, and must be allowed plenty of time to sleep and rest when the games are over. Allowing an older child to be responsible for the cat's feeding and grooming will do much to encourage a love and a sense of responsibility for pets.

MEETING OTHER FAMILY PETS

Introducing your new kitten to cats and dogs that are already established in the household may present problems. Prepare to face a certain amount of ill will and try to minimise jealousy by not making too much fuss over the newcomer. With cats, after a day or two of spitting and growling at a new member of the family, things usually settle down and after the initial strangeness has worn off they quite obviously enjoy the company of one of their kind and get much more fun out of life. Having said this, however, there are occasionally cases where cats prove to be completely incompatible and the only kind solution is to try and find another home for the newcomer.

Meeting
dogs

In the case of a dog that is not accustomed to cats it is obviously necessary to take more care. Many dogs have a strong hunting instinct when it comes to small animals that run away and they regard them as legitimate prey. A young kitten might easily be injured or even killed in the first few moments. Even if they appear to have accepted each other, it is not wise to leave a dog alone with a young kitten for any time or to feed the two together. However, once friendship becomes established cats and dogs usually get on very well together, often sharing the same basket and washing each other, although the dog may still feel justified in chasing other people's cats. Indeed, it is true to say that in most homes in the end it is the cat that seems to rule the roost.

HIS OWN CORNER & HIS OWN BED

Warmth is of the greatest importance in the care of young animals and in winter it is best to keep your kitten in a constant, even, warm temperature away from draughts (ideally in the kitchen). If the bed or box is placed against a radiator, stove, or other source of heat the newcomer will usually adopt it as his own and settle down very comfortably to sleep.

Bed or
box?

A bed of his own gives a great sense of security to a kitten in a strange new home.

A cardboard box with one side cut down to provide a step and the other sides left high to keep out draughts is suitable, or you can place the box on its side to produce a completely roofed house. These have the great advantage of being inexpensive and easy to replace. However, if you or your cat would like something a little more elaborate there are many different types of bed to be found nowadays at pet stores, from the traditional basketwork to the modern polystyrene shape with a plastic cover (the latter have the advantage of being easily sponged clean) but as a general rule a cat will feel safer and more content in a bed with high sides.

a) A simple bed made from a cut-down cardboard box

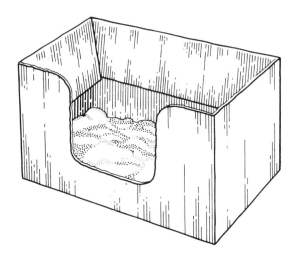

b) Placing a wooden or cardboard box on its side may make a roofed bed

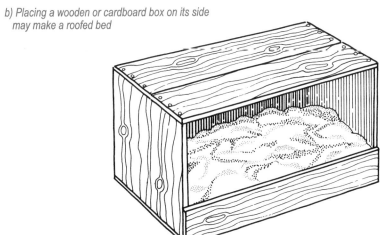

BLANKETS & BEDDING

Cats love comfort and they will appreciate a pillow or a blanket in their bed, often quite visibly expressing their pleasure at new soft bedding by treading, or kneading the ground and purring loudly. However, it is best to use either a polystyrene foam square covered by a blanket or a plastic cushion since flock or feather pillows may harbour fleas. The bed covers should be washed regularly, or alternatively you can use pieces of old quilted dressing gowns, or other remnants that can be discarded and burnt.

FEEDING KITTENS

Proper diet

The kitten has a very high dietary requirement compared to the adult cat. Because it is growing quickly it needs food not only to supply body heat and energy but also to form tissues and bones. In fact a kitten of seven weeks old may eat the equivalent of 20% of its own bodyweight in food each day.

Meat

Cats are naturally total carnivores (meat eaters) and have a very high requirement of protein and fat in the diet. In the wild state it would be small mammals that form their prey. It is also worth knowing that in the wild, cats probably took very little water as such (they were originally desert dwellers) since fresh animal carcasses contain approximately 90% of fluid and this supplied sufficient for their needs. Carbohydrate is not a normal constituent of the diet of the cat since they use protein to supply energy, but it can be used as a food supplement to supply bulk if given in conjunction with a high protein food.

VITAMINS & MINERALS

Balanced diet

Cats have a rather higher requirement of vitamins A, D, and B12 than other animals, and the growing kitten and the pregnant cat especially require calcium. However, all these elements will be found in adequate amounts in a normal balanced diet and harm can be caused by over-administration of vitamins. If you suspect that your kitten may be suffering from a deficiency condition seek Veterinary advice rather than attempt to remedy the situation yourself before diagnosis.

WHEN TO FEED

At first, "little and often" is the best rule.
A general guide:

Age	Total daily amount of a high protein food (canned or fresh)		No. of meals
7 - 12 wks	3 - 5 oz	divided into	4
3 - 6 mths	5 - 7 oz	divided into	3
6 - 12 mths	7 - 71/2 oz	divided into	2

Lactol or milk may be given in addition to the stated amounts.

Feeding guide

The table above is intended only as a general rule and the amounts of food mentioned are average figures. Individual animals may vary considerably in their food requirements, not only according to their age, health and the conditions of their life, but also according to their metabolic rate (that is the rate at which each animal converts food into heat and energy). If you feel unhappy about your kitten's growth or progress always consult your own Veterinary Surgeon.

FRESH FOODS

All fresh meats and offal supply protein and fat. Lungs (lights) can be used occasionally but they have a poor food content and while they are obviously palatable and very popular with cats, they are not really suitable for growing kittens. Cheese is a good source of protein and is well accepted by many cats. Milk (as fresh milk or Lactol) is a good source of protein and also of calcium and vitamin D. However, milk soon deteriorates if it is left in the dish, so if your kitten does not finish the drink, take it up and throw it away.

Milk

Very occasionally cats develop an intolerance to the lactose found in cow's milk, resulting in diarrhoea. If this happens cows milk should be removed from the diet.

PREPARED MANUFACTURED FOODS

Nowadays, the majority of cats are fed on convenience manufactured foods (this subject is covered more fully in Chapter 4 - Caring for the Adult Cat). They are very carefully formulated to provide a balanced food, with the appropriate vitamins and minerals. If given in accordance with the instructions they should provide a suitable diet for a normal kitten. They are, as a rule, very palatable and have the great advantage of being readily available and easy to prepare.

If wished, fresh or raw foods can be used to supplement a diet of prepared foods but there is no evidence to show that this is necessary.

Water

Although the water consumption of some cats is very low, water should be available at all times and it is especially important in hot weather, or if a dry or semi-moist food is being used.

FEEDING THE NEW ARRIVAL

When your new kitten arrives he may feel strange and uncertain in his new surroundings or he may be unused to the type of food that you are offering. The best policy is to offer not more than a teaspoonful of some very palatable food on a saucer (well-cooked and boned rabbit, cooked giblets, or white fish are all highly acceptable) and to wait until this has been finished before offering more. It is better that the kitten should be slightly under, rather than over-fed, until it has adjusted to the new routine. A sudden change in diet may induce diarrhoea, so any change must be gradual.

For very young kittens, sieved baby foods (meat or fish) can be used and can be given with a spoon if necessary.

The right amount

Once a satisfactory feeding routine has been established, make it a rule to put down the amount of food that you expect to be eaten at each feeding time and if it is not all cleared up, promptly remove it until the next meal is due. If your kitten seems perfectly fit and playful and yet food is being left at each meal, you are probably over-estimating his or her requirements and you should reduce the amount of each meal accordingly.

Healthy cats do not simply become bored with a food that they have previously enjoyed unless they are being over-fed, so avoid falling into the trap of searching for new foods to tempt the jaded appetite of a cat who has already eaten quite enough.

FEEDING DISHES

In the interest of hygiene your kitten should have his own feeding dishes which are kept separate. Old saucers will certainly serve the purpose but the plastic dishes sold at pet shops (in a non tip-over design) are inexpensive and, since they are unbreakable, last for years.

WARNING

Dehydration

Young kittens which arrive at their new home in the early stages of gastro-enteritis infection may refuse to eat any food and if not given prompt Veterinary treatment will probably quickly become dehydrated and weak. They may die. If you suspect that this may be the case with your new kitten, consult a Veterinary Surgeon as soon as possible. In the meantime, keep the patient very warm and try to give a few drops of water every hour with a dropper (see Chapter 6 on Treatment & First Aid).

TRAINING

Cats are not, as a rule, as easily trained as dogs. They have a greater sense of independence and are less concerned with pleasing their owners. Sometimes a battle of wills may be needed before a satisfactory code of behaviour is established. Remember that your cat will be a much more enjoyable member of the family if he has learned some basic good manners. However, since cats do not bark at night or chew up shoes, they do start with some built-in advantages.

TOILET TRAINING

This is the first and most important lesson if your cat is to have the freedom of the house.

Taught by mother

Cats are naturally very clean animals and some kittens (especially those that have remained with the mother cat to the age of eight weeks or more) may have already acquired some idea of house-training before they reach their home. If your kitten is among this number you are very lucky.

However, in the case of kittens which have been living wild, or have had several unsatisfactory homes, the situation is very different and unfortunately bad habits, once learned, can be hard to lose.

Patience is essential

Patience is the most important factor in training or in re-training a cat. They are timid animals and if you become angry and shout, or if you hit your cat for soiling the floors, you may simply create a neurotic pet who will never fully recover its confidence in the world.

TRAY OR GARDEN

In almost all cases it is necessary to train a cat at first to use a litter tray, even if you hope later to let it use a garden. If you are a keen gardener yourself (or even more important, if your neighbours are) it may be worthwhile continuing to empty a tray once or twice daily, rather than have the nuisance and the problems that result from having a cat dig up gardens. In any case, in bad weather and through the night a tray will be necessary for the first few weeks and it can be a great help when moving house, or putting a cat into a cattery, if he is still accustomed to using a tray.

There are two very important rules to observe in training a cat to be house clean: -

The rules

1. See that he is confined to one room only until the idea of using the litter tray is thoroughly imprinted on his mind.

Young animals have only very limited control over bladder and bowels and if a kitten is allowed the freedom of the house, or is shut in a room with carpets for some hours, accidents can be expected. Once carpets have become soiled with urine cats, like puppies, have a tendency to assume that this is an appropriate place and return to it. If the kitten is kept in one room with an impervious floor which can be properly washed and disinfected, the nuisance will be kept to a minimum.

2. Provide a suitable litter tray. See that it remains always in the same place (preferably in a quiet corner of the kitchen) and see that the litter is changed as often as necessary. Cats are very

fastidious animals and are reluctant to use a soiled tray. Once clean habits are established it may be possible to remove the tray from the kitchen to a garage or basement if preferred but beware of upsetting your cat's routine too soon.

Litter trays

Proper plastic litter trays are now available from almost all pet shops. This should be lined with a strong layer of newspaper or a litter tray liner and then add a good scattering of a prepared cat litter, or earth if litter is not available. Some cats are inclined to scratch rather vigorously in their litter, scattering it on the floor, so it may be a good idea to place the tray in a large flat cardboard box lid to reduce the mess. The tray should be washed with disinfectant solution each week.

Put the kitten onto the tray after every mealtime, whenever it wakes up, or at any other time when you think it may be necessary. Sherley's Swiftie Trainer sprinkled in the tray often helps to start the right habit.

If the kitten makes a mess elsewhere in the room, take it to the spot and reprimand it in a very cross tone of voice, but without shouting. It is not necessary to smack a cat - your tone of voice will make it quite clear.

Garden

Having once trained your cat to use a tray it can sometimes be difficult to retrain it to use the garden, especially in cold weather. However, in most cases with the return of summer, when the cat can spend long hours in the garden, the problem usually resolves of its own accord, although it may sometimes help if the litter tray is placed outside the back door for a while.

TRAINING YOUR KITTEN TO COME WHEN CALLED

This is an important lesson but it is not, by any means, as easy as when training a puppy. The psychology of the cat is very different; he does not respond automatically to the sound of the owner's voice but quite sensibly makes a reasoned judgement as to whether it is in his own interest to come at that time.

Rewards

However, much can be done to induce a reflex tendency to come when called by use of rewards. Find something that your cat really enjoys, perhaps a meaty biscuit, a tiny piece of cheese, or a Sherley's Top Form Cat Treat, and he will soon come to associate the particular tone of voice when you call with the treat (and it is, of course, important to always give the treat if the system is to work). This habit, once established, can save a great deal of annoyance on those occasions when it is essential to get your cat in a hurry. However, be warned, it will not work well with the overfed cat, or the one which is allowed to pick at food all day.

Do train your cat not to sit on furniture. It can be done if you start out with determination and check him every time he tries to get on a chair. He has his own comfortable bed, so there is no need to feel sorry for him and it is not pleasant to find that clothes are covered with cat hair.

If your will power is not quite up to this, at least make sure that your cat sleeps in just one chair of the house.

Claws

The bad habit that causes the most annoyance to owners is scratching or clawing at furniture, carpets, or sometimes even wallpaper. Siamese are probably the worst culprits (and they have very strong nails) and with an adult cat the habit may prove incurable. It is particularly difficult because to the cat his behaviour is a perfectly normal method of sharpening his claws and he probably finds it odd that his owner objects so much. Boredom is often the main cause of this type of destructiveness. A cat which has a garden to wander in and trees to climb usually learns to sharpen his claws in the outside world but this, of course, is of little comfort to the flat dweller with a well loved but destructive pet.

Scratching post

With a young kitten, every possible effort must be made to let him know that this behaviour is unacceptable. Check him at once if he is caught in the act with a stern tone of voice. See that the nails are not allowed to grow too long. Cut just the tips yourself with nail clippers, or if you feel uncertain of how to do this, visit your Veterinary Surgeon and ask to be shown (also see Nails in Chapter 4 - Caring for the Adult Cat). Provide a scratching post. You can buy prepared scratching posts from pet shops. These are impregnated with a substance that is attractive to cats and so encourages the use. Alternatively, use a fallen tree bough that you may perhaps keep in the garage or in the kitchen. As far as possible, see that your cat is not left alone in rooms where there is furniture to damage.

GROOMING

As soon as you bring home your new fluffy kitten you should also buy a brush and comb and establish a regular grooming routine, once weekly for short-haired varieties and daily for Persian and other long-haired varieties (see Chapter 4 - Caring for the Adult Cat). A strong nylon brush and a fine comb (either steel or plastic) are essential tools. Spread a thick layer of newspaper on a table in a good light, and apart from combing out tangles, check the following: -

1. Check the eyes and nose for any discharge. Staining around the eyes is sometimes a problem with white cats, and Sherley's Eye Lotion may be of use. However, if there is any redness, soreness, or excessive watering consult your Veterinary Surgeon.

2. Check the ears for the presence of dark wax which may denote the presence of ear mites (see Chapter 5) or any discharge. The ears can be cleaned with Sherley's Ear Cleaner, a specially formulated solution that helps prevent the build up of wax and other debris in the ear.

3. Check the coat for fleas, lice, and ticks (see Chapter 5).

4. Check the nails. If too long the end can be "tipped" with nail cutters.

Grooming should not be an ordeal that your cat dreads, provided you approach it sensibly. Spend a little time combing the ticklish areas under the chin and behind the ears (which they usually enjoy) as well as carrying out the more serious work.

MEDICAL CARE

Worms

Young kittens generally have roundworms and, less frequently, tapeworms. See Chapter 5 for recognition and treatment and other parasites including fleas, lice, ear mites, and so on.

TEETHING - See Chapter 7

VACCINATION

Feline enteritis

1. Enteritis vaccination has been carried out for a number of years and appears to provide an effective level of immunity against viral gastro-enteritis, a very serious and often fatal disease characterised by high temperature, vomiting and diarrhoea (see Chapter 7). It is a condition that is encountered most in boarding kennels or breeding catteries and for this reason most proprietors of catteries insist on a certificate of vaccination before admitting cats for boarding.

Vaccination is usually carried out from nine weeks old, and thereafter booster injections are necessary once a year.

Influenza

2. Vaccination against feline influenza is also recommended. This is usually a course of two injections and can be carried out from nine weeks of age. Once again, booster injections are necessary.

Since this serious, and potentially fatal, disease occurs most often in catteries, vaccination is strongly recommended for anyone who may have to board their pet during holidays. Remember to consult your Veterinary Surgeon in good time to obtain maximum protection.

NEUTERING - PREVENTING THE CAT POPULATION EXPLOSION

Many new cat owners may feel reluctant to consider having their kitten neutered but there really are sound reasons in favour, both for the male and the female.

THE FEMALE CAT

The female cat will, if allowed, have several litters each year, often becoming pregnant again before she has finished feeding the last litter. One cat may, in her lifetime, be responsible for hundreds of offspring. Apart from the fact that this over-production exhausts the mother cat and shortens her life, there simply are not sufficient kind and caring homes to take in all these newcomers. No cat lover would want to bring kittens into the world to end as hungry and unwanted strays.

OESTRUS OR SEASON

Calling

The female kitten comes into season (or "calling" as it is also known, because she really does develop a very loud and persistent miaow, quite different from the usual sound) at six months or soon after. If allowed out, she will almost certainly become pregnant. Keeping a cat in at this time is far from easy since she is, of course, determined to get out and may become very irritable and even bad tempered. Worse still, you will usually find that several of the local toms have arrived on the doorstep or even in the house, if they have the opportunity.

THE OPERATION

Neutering, or spaying, involves a surgical operation under a general anaesthetic. The uterus and the ovaries are removed to prevent the cat from coming into season or becoming pregnant.

Age

This operation is usually carried out from twenty weeks old onwards. Opinions vary slightly as to the best time, so consult your own Veterinary Surgeon. If you have decided not to breed, before six months is safest to avoid the risk of pregnancy. However, if you decide you would like to rear one litter the operation may be carried out later and, as a rule, causes the cat remarkably little distress or disturbance.

In most instances you will be asked to bring your cat to the Veterinary Surgeon first thing in the morning, after having starved her for at least twelve hours (this is to avoid the risk of vomiting whilst under the anaesthetic), and you may be able to collect her the same evening or on the following day. Your own Veterinary Surgeon will give you more precise instructions if you ask but, as a rule, with a little extra care and attention for the first day or two, your cat will soon be her playful self again.

The cat may well be a little sleepy when returned to you but this is, of course, perfectly normal after a general anaesthetic. It is best to keep the patient in a confined space (ideally in a cat basket) and in a warm atmosphere for the first few hours.

Feeding

Do not be in too much of a hurry to offer food. Many cats arrive home feeling fit and hungry and demand a meal, but it is usually better to offer either warm milk or an absolute minimum of food. Over-eating may lead to vomiting and that is both painful and dangerous after an abdominal operation.

Stitch
removal

In most cases the female will have one or more stitches, either on the flank or under the abdomen, which the Veterinary Surgeon will remove after seven to ten days. Cats are much less inclined than dogs to remove their own stitches but they should, if possible, be prevented from biting or pulling at them. It may be necessary, in some cases, to construct a cotton jacket to cover the stitches since it is not easy to keep an abdominal bandage on a cat.

CHEMOTHERAPEUTIC METHODS

Oestrus and pregnancy can be prevented or postponed by means of a chemical given by injection or tablet. This is helpful for an owner who thinks that they might like to have a litter at some more convenient time, or who is very reluctant to face the thought of an operation. However, the treatment must be repeated at intervals during the year throughout her life and for the average owner it is not as satisfactory or as free from complications as the surgical method.

THE MALE CAT

Male cats are neutered partly for their own welfare and partly to make them more suitable as household pets.

Mature male cats tend to wander away in search of females, sometimes becoming lost and ending up as strays and frequently being injured or killed on the roads. They have a strong instinct to fight other males in their territory and as a consequence suffer severe wounds and abscesses, often looking battered and battle scarred before they are no more than two years old.

There is also the disadvantage from the owner's point of view that the urine of the unneutered male develops a characteristically strong, unpleasant and persistent odour. In the breeding season even house-trained males are liable to urinate or "spray" in their own homes.

Neutering is a simple operation in the male. It is carried out under general anaesthetic and is usually free from side effects, with no stitches.

Age

The operation is usually carried out from five to eight months, although adult males may also be neutered. At the younger age the operation is scarcely noticed but some opinions favour waiting until the cat is more mature. While the operation is not generally an abdominal one, the cat may feel a little "groggy" on returning home and should be given the same general post-operative care as the female. Consult your own Veterinary Surgeon on this.

Neutering in the male or female does not produce a fat or sluggish cat. This is a result of over-feeding. With proper care and management the neutered cat should have a long, active, and happy life.

MONORCHIDS & CRYPTORCHIDS

In male cats either one, or both, testicles may be retained in the abdomen. In this case your Veterinary Surgeon may either advise you to wait for six months and then return your cat for another examination or, if the cat is more mature, may suggest an abdominal operation, since a cat which has one abdominal testicle could show all the undesirable characteristics of a full tom.

CHAPTER 4

CARING FOR THE ADULT CAT

Adoption

People become owners of adult cats for two reasons; either they adopt a cat, or almost as frequently a cat adopts them. It seems that cats have an instinct that leads them to homes where they will be welcome. The usual picture is that a rather hungry looking cat is seen hanging about in the garden. If it is fed its appearances become more frequent, until almost imperceptibly it becomes established as a regular member of the family. It is sometimes rather hard to determine the reason for this movement in the cat population. Some that are obviously hungry and uncared for may have come from bad homes, or they may be unneutered toms who have wandered too far away in search of females and become lost. In other cases it seems that they did not like their original home; perhaps there was a child or dog who made life difficult for them and they simply moved on to find somewhere more to their liking.

Problems

A cat that has had one good home will usually change owners without too much stress providing that conditions are similar. However, adopting a cat which has been badly treated, or which has been wandering and fending for itself for some time can present problems. Even after years of kindness and regular feeding it may still become terrified if it is shut in a room or if it hears a sudden noise or a strange voice.

HOW LONG SHOULD YOU KEEP HIM IN?

It is almost impossible to make a definite rule as to how long a cat should be kept in his new home before it can be considered safe to let him out alone. Much depends on the area and whether there is heavy traffic that may constitute a danger and also on the temperament of the cat; a nervous cat may easily bolt if it is startled and try to return to its original home.

If your cat will wear a harness or a collar and lead (as many Siamese do) it is a good plan to walk him round the new garden under supervision, allowing plenty of time for him to inspect and smell everything, before he is given his first taste of freedom.

UNDERSTANDING THE PSYCHOLOGY OF THE CAT

In the normal healthy cat, hunger is a strong controlling factor, so when you let your new pet outside alone for the first time see that it is just before a mealtime is due. In this way you can be certain that however interesting the outside world may seem he will be strongly motivated to return home.

If you live near a busy road do not make the mistake of thinking that your cat will remain safely in the back garden. They are extremely inquisitive animals and inevitably in time their curiosity will cause them to wander further afield and into danger.

It may be worth considering constructing a wire netting enclosure in the garden to allow your cat a little freedom and fresh air without risk, as we advise for kittens (see Chapter 3).

LIVING IN A FLAT

A flat is not the ideal place to keep a cat, unless it has some access to the outside, even if it is only over the roofs for exercise purposes. If it is a case of rescuing a stray it is certainly true that a kind home in a flat is better than no home at all but unfortunately, if conditions are too restricted, cats become bored. It is then that destructive habits such as clawing furniture, or even wallpaper, are likely to be a problem.

PUTTING THE CAT OUT

At one time it was accepted practice to put the cat out at night - regardless of the weather - but in today's heavy traffic, many owners prefer to keep their pets in.

If you feel happier to know that your cat is safely inside at night try to call him each evening at the same time and reward his return with a few cat biscuits, a piece of cheese, a Top Form Cat Treat, or some other treat. This produces what is known as a conditioned reflex that may become so accurate as to make you suspect that your cat has his own little wristwatch!

CAT DOORS

For cats that persistently come home late, or for those who are always on the wrong side of the door asking to come in, the cat flap may prove to be the answer. This consists of a small flap, just large enough to admit a cat, which is let into one of the lower panels of the house door (these can now be bought pre-fabricated at pet stores and hardware shops). They are certainly a help to

A cat flap let into a door. Make sure it is placed low enough for your cat to step through

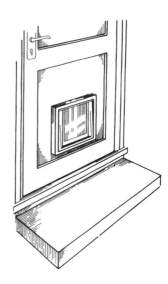

owners who have to be away from home for hours at a time and can thus allow their cat some freedom knowing that it will be able to come in if the weather changes. They do have a slight disadvantage that some cats are inclined to invite their less reputable feline friends in as well, although there are more advanced flaps with magnetic locks that recognise small attachments on your cat's collar and only let him in.

Cat shelters

If your cat is reluctant to use the cat flap at first, try leaving it wedged open for a few days until the cat accepts that it is the normal route of entry.

If it is not possible to fit a cat flap in any of your doors it may be worth considering the construction of a cat shelter. This could be a small wooden waterproof "house" with a cat flap in it, lined with a warm material. While your cat is waiting for you to get home, or if the weather takes a turn for the worse, he will have somewhere warm and dry to shelter.

NAME AND ADDRESS

Tag

As soon as your new cat arrives buy him a collar and identification tag or a Sherley's Lost & Found Identification Collar (see Chapter 3). There is always a risk that an adult cat may try to return to his previous home and this is the first place to enquire if he should become lost, assuming the distance is reasonable.

HEALTH CHECKS FOR THE NEW ARRIVAL

If your new adult cat comes from a friend or a neighbour he will probably be healthy and you will be able to check on any past history of vaccination, neutering, or illness. With a genuine stray a health check may present more problems.

THINGS TO LOOK FOR

If your new cat seems listless, ill, or unable to eat, consult a Veterinary Surgeon as soon as possible. If you are unable to pay the fees of a private Veterinary Surgeon, look out for a clinic run by the PDSA, RSPCA, Blue Cross, or other welfare organisations, where you can obtain advice or help either free or at little cost.

Flu

Sneezing, sore or runny nose and eyes may indicate flu, or catarrhal infection (chronic sinusitis).

Ears

Shaking the head, scratching the ears, or bare places behind the ears may indicate an ear mite infection (see Chapter 5).

Fleas

Poor coat or bare patches in the fur may indicate the presence of fleas or other parasites. A spray with Sherley's Big Red Flea Spray or dusting with Sherley's Permethrin Flea Powder should correct this (see Chapter 5). You can also fit a Sherley's Flea Collar to provide continued protection, but if you have used a spray or powder, you must first wait the number of days specified on the label before fitting a collar. If the skin condition does not respond to your first aid measures quite quickly consult a Veterinary Surgeon who will advise you if other treatment is required.

Fighting

Unneutered male cats are often covered with wounds, scratches, or even abscesses as a result of fighting (see Chapter 7 for advice on treatment). If your newly adopted tom is to become a family pet it is best to have him neutered or he may wander away again to join the ranks of the homeless cats.

Worms

Cats that have been living wild and eating mice and other rodents are often infested with tapeworm. A routine dosing with Sherley's Worming Granules is a wise precaution (see Chapter 5).

NEUTERING

In the case of a male cat your Veterinary Surgeon will be able to tell you if he has been neutered if you are unsure, but in the case of the female it is not always possible to be certain. In many cases young female cats which are straying are found to be in kitten and the new owner may find that they have suddenly a large family to care for. However, since kittens are not always easy to find homes for it is as well to have the newcomer neutered (spayed) as soon as possible (see Chapter 3).

Vaccination

If your new cat comes from a good home you will probably find that it has been immunised against viral enteritis and cat flu (see Chapter 3) but it may require booster injections.

In the case of a stray it is unlikely to have received any protection of this kind and it is best to consult your Veterinary Surgeon to decide when vaccination should be carried out.

TRAINING A NEW ARRIVAL

Own bed

Establishing a code of behaviour can present problems with an adult cat but it is important if he is to fit in as a member of the new family. For the first week at least it is probably best to confine the cat to one room, preferably the kitchen. Provide him with his own comfortable bed and he will have no excuse to sleep on yours. If it is placed in a quiet warm spot he will soon settle and feel at home. If there are dogs and children in the house a raised shelf may allow the newcomer more security and peace of mind. It may be a good idea to pin a notice on the kitchen door saying "Cat within - please close doors" to remind everyone in the house.

It will almost certainly be necessary to put a litter tray down for the first few days (see Chapter 3) and this can present problems at first for an older cat that has been trained to go out. However, if the box or tray is put in a quiet corner of the room and the cat is left undisturbed the situation will usually resolve without too much trouble. Some adult cats may prefer peat or soil in their litter trays before being introduced gradually to normal cat litter.

If you do not intend your cat to sit on the chairs you must be firm and persistent about this from the start but try to avoid shouting or frightening him. He may have come from a home where standards were very different and will find it hard to understand new rules and commands.

BAD HABITS

Unfortunately, an adult cat may have acquired bad habits that can be hard to deal with. As far as most owners are concerned, scratching or sharpening claws on furniture is the most serious (see Chapter 3).

Scratching post

See that your cat has as much freedom and exercise outside as possible. Provide him with an indoor scratching post for times when he must stay in. See that the claws are kept reasonably short - but if all these measures prove ineffective simply resolve to see that he is never left unsupervised in any room where damage may be done. If it proves impossible to reform your cat completely, at least you can keep damage to a minimum.

Cats that are dirty in the house present a serious problem. As a species they normally tend to be almost obsessively clean and modest in their habits, but if as a result of illness, change of home, or some emotional stress, their training breaks down, the situation may be difficult to remedy. Consult your Veterinary Surgeon to check if there is any physical cause for the behaviour. If this is not the case, consider installing a cat door to allow easy access to the outside, see that there is always a clean litter tray available and resign yourself to confining the cat to one room only in the house, where the minimum of damage will result.

Birds

Killing birds, while it cannot strictly be called a bad habit since it is a normal instinct for cats, can be very upsetting for bird lovers. The most effective way to deal with this is to put a bell on the collar. After all, a civilised well-fed cat is killing purely for pleasure and to prevent this as far as possible is not unreasonable or unkind.

Stealing

Unfortunately, even very well fed cats are inclined to steal if they get the opportunity. See that, as far as possible, food is not left out to provide temptation but also make a strict rule that your cat is never allowed to jump onto tables or work surfaces. If he attempts to do so clap your hands sharply and say "No". This is in the cat's own interests as well since each year many cats suffer burns as a result of jumping onto hot electric cooker plates, or dislodging pans of hot food.

FEEDING

Choosy cats

When a stray cat is taken in it is, as a rule, hungry and will gratefully eat any food that it is offered. However, there is a natural tendency on the part of the owner to make up for past deprivation by feeding to capacity with the result that the once hungry cat becomes choosy and starts to refuse foods that it previously enjoyed. In many cases this sets up a cycle in which the owner searches for new and interesting foods which the cat at first enjoys and then, as it becomes satiated, rejects. In desperation the owner may buy vitamin pills or consult a Veterinary Surgeon to induce the supposedly under-nourished cat to eat.

Normal

Certainly no-one would wish that cats should go hungry and this kind of rather obsessional behaviour on the part of cat owners is usually a harmless foible. On the other hand, there really is no need to create a faddy and demanding monster out of a perfectly normal cat. It is not even necessary to supply changes in the diet (although all cats enjoy an occasional treat of leftover meat or game in their food). If a good high protein canned or packaged food is supplied in the correct amounts, a normal healthy cat will eat and enjoy its food every day. Variety does not seem to be a requirement.

If your cat seems listless and rejects his food, or if he has difficulty in chewing or swallowing, you should consult a Veterinary Surgeon as soon as possible, but if your healthy, lively cat starts to reject his meals the answer lies in your own hands. Reduce the amount given at each meal drastically until the appetite returns and check that he is not obtaining food elsewhere, e.g. from a neighbour.

NUTRITIONAL REQUIREMENTS

In the wild state, the cat would have lived entirely on the small rodents or birds that he was able to kill. These supplied not only the protein, fat, vitamins and minerals that he required, but also the greater part of the fluid content of the diet.

In the civilised world the cat still has a very high dietary requirement of protein and, unlike the dog, he is not able to substitute carbohydrate for this to any great extent without losing condition. He also has a higher fat requirement than the dog and fat added to prepared cat foods greatly increases the palatability.

Vitamins & minerals

The normal adult cat will find his needs for vitamins and minerals are supplied adequately in a balanced diet (as suggested below) but for the pregnant or lactating cat (see Chapter 2), or for the growing kitten (see Chapter 3), or following illness, a supplement may be advisable, e.g. Sherley's Vionate.

WHAT TO FEED

Balanced diet

Over the last forty years there has been an almost revolutionary change in the feeding of cats - mainly for the better. Where previously most cats were fed a diet of meat scraps, lights, or white fish (often deficient in protein and vitamins), nowadays the great proportion are fed on pre-packaged manufactured foods. While these are not necessarily better than good quality meat and fish, they have been carefully formulated to provide a balanced meal for the average cat, they are readily available, easy to store and prepare, and probably overall are a lot cheaper than any equivalent food.

FRESH FOODS

Meat

Meat and offal of all kinds can be fed (cooked or raw), although it should be remembered that lights (lungs) are low in protein value and should not be given as a total diet.

Liver

Liver is rich in Vitamin A; a vitamin that the cat is not able to synthesise and which is essential for good health. It makes a good addition to the diet if given once a week. However, some vitamins in excess can cause harm and an exclusive diet of liver can rapidly lead to severe disorders in the skeletal system.

Rabbit

Rabbit and game of all kinds are very popular with cats and are ideal for tempting the appetite of a sick cat.

Fish

Fish is a useful food, though if white fish is used as the only food it can lead to vitamin deficiency. It is best prepared in a pressure cooker and the softened bones provide a good source of minerals for the pregnant cat. Canned fish such as pilchards or sardines have a good food value and surprisingly many cats seem to enjoy the tomato sauce as well, but they should not be fed exclusively.

Cheese

Cheese is a good source of protein and is well accepted by most cats. Vegetable protein (Soya, etc) can be used only as a partial substitute for animal protein in the diet. On no account should any attempt be made to feed a cat a "vegetarian" diet.

Vegetables

The cat is able to synthesise its own supply of vitamin C and green vegetables are not necessary in the diet, although as many owners will have noticed, some cats like to eat grass, while others have even more exotic tastes and enjoy cucumber and other vegetables without any ill effects.

Bones

Cats enjoy bones to eat almost as much as dogs and since they are more careful and fastidious feeders and do not bolt their food, they suffer much less from the results of swallowing sharp or indigestible fragments. However, large bones can become wedged in the mouth or throat so they should be avoided if possible.

Bread

Carbohydrates (bread, non-meat biscuit meal) are not a normal constituent of the cat's diet but small amounts can be added to the food, providing that it also contains an adequate amount of protein.

CANNED FOODS

The canned foods (meat, fish, rabbit, etc) which are prepared by leading manufacturers are carefully and scientifically formulated to supply a total food for a normal cat and they can provide a very satisfactory and trouble-free method of feeding throughout a cat's life. Care of course should be taken, as with any canned food, to see that once it is opened it is not exposed to contamination and it is better if part of a tin has been refrigerated to allow it to return to room temperature before feeding.

SEMI-MOIST

The semi-moist types of food are a relatively recent addition to the cat's menu and they are a more concentrated food. It should be remembered that fresh foods contain over 90% of water, so if a semi-moist food is introduced, it is important to see that the cat is receiving sufficient additional fluid in the diet in the form of milk or preferably water. However, this type of food seems to be very palatable and well accepted by cats. It is particularly easy to store and use.

DRY FOODS - CAT BISCUIT

This is a food with a high protein and fat content that most cats enjoy very much. However, it is more concentrated and has an even lower fluid content than the semi-moist food and suffers from the same disadvantages. It is therefore essential to ensure that a ready supply of clean fresh water is available at all times for your cat to drink.

LIQUIDS

Milk

Milk is an important food for the young kitten and, while it is not necessary for the adult cat, it is obvious that many of them enjoy it. Fresh milk or Sherley's Lactol are useful foods in convalescence and for the lactating female with a litter to feed.

Occasionally, intolerance to lactose in cow's milk is seen in some cats and it seems that it may cause digestive disorders, especially in Siamese cats. However, contrary to the old wives' tale, cow's milk is not a source of roundworms.

Water

Although, as we have seen, many cats drink very little water, it is important to see that it is always available, especially in hot weather, or when feeding a dry food with a low moisture content. On some occasions, cats develop a particular liking for running water and prefer to drink from a running tap.

AMOUNTS TO FEED

General guide

It is not possible to lay down definite rules on feeding, since even within the species, conditions of life and dietary requirements can vary. For instance, the young growing cat requires proportionally much more food than the mature adult does. However, as a general guide, most adult cats require between five to eight ounces (150 to 250 grammes) daily of a high protein food, according to weight. In practice this works out as half a tin of cat food twice daily for the average small cat (with milk as well if wanted). The larger cat requires the same amount with the addition of a small quantity of cat biscuit, or household fish or meat scraps if they are available. Remember, of course, that if your particular cat does not appear to make satisfactory progress it is essential to visit your Veterinary Surgeon for guidance suited to the individual case.

HOW OFTEN TO FEED

Number of meals

In the wild state the cat would probably have eaten only once in 24 hours but under home conditions most owners find it more satisfactory to divide the meal and feed twice, while for young kittens or pregnant cats at least three meals daily are necessary (see Chapters 2 and 3).

Food should not be left down all day and in particular biscuits should not be left to be nibbled as well. This is a certain way to ruin an appetite and to produce an obese cat. If a meal is not finished at once it should be picked up and nothing further offered until the next mealtime. Overeating is just as harmful for cats as it is for humans and makes them prematurely old. By giving your cat a well balanced diet without excess you will increase his chances of a long, active, and healthy life.

GROOMING

While grooming dogs is accepted as normal part of ownership there is a tendency for owners to assume that cats need no attention at all. Unfortunately, this is far from the truth.

Some shorthaired cats do keep themselves very trim, with constant licking and grooming, but during the moulting season even they are unable to cope with the enormous amounts of hair which is either shed onto the carpets and furniture or, worse still, swallowed.

Persians and other longhaired cats require very much more attention and must be regarded as a time-absorbing hobby.

Moulting

In the wild state it is probable that cats had one heavy moult during the hot summer months and then grew a new coat for the winter. Today, with the increase in central heating most owners will agree that moulting seems to take place throughout the year. However, for a quick and complete moult, that leaves the coat silky and shiny, Sherley's Anti-Moult Drops can be used.

Regular grooming is essential - for smooth hairs weekly, for long coats three times weekly or, if they are to be kept in show condition, daily.

START OUT THE RIGHT WAY

Choose a suitable place for grooming, if possible a utility room, outhouse, or garage to avoid the nuisance of flying hairs in the house. Check that all doors and windows are securely shut and place your cat on a table of comfortable height with a non-slip surface if possible.

The right tools

You will need: -

A fine-toothed, strong steel comb and a brush (a strong nylon hairbrush is ideal).
A pair of blunt-ended scissors and nail clippers.
Sherley's Eye Lotion and Ear Cleaner or similar plus cotton wool to remove any discharge from eyes and ears.
An insecticidal dusting powder such as Sherley's Permethrin Flea Powder.
A grooming aid such as Sherley's Grooming Spray.

Matts

Start with the comb first to remove any tangles. Work down from the head, under the chin and behind the ears, then down the back and tail. Finally, turn the cat on his back and groom underneath. Then follow with a brushing to remove the loose and dead hair. In a shorthaired cat this is quite a simple process as a rule, but with a longhaired cat (especially in the moulting season) if the coat has been neglected, there may be not only tangles but thick felt-like matts, especially behind the ears, at the base of the spine, and under the abdomen, which can be extremely difficult to remove. The best method of dealing with this problem is to raise the matted lumps of hair away from the skin gently with the comb and try and tease them apart. If this fails, cut the underlying hair using blunt-ended scissors (taking great care not to cut the cat in the process). This will, of course, for a while, leave unsightly bare patches, but the hair grows again very quickly and the comfort and well-being of the cat are of much more importance than his appearance.

Not a one man job

It need hardly be said that, unless the cat is a very placid one, this task requires two people, so try to get a friend to help.

Removing severe tangles can prove very painful for the cat and very difficult for the owner. If it really seems insurmountable consult your Veterinary Surgeon. He may be willing to arrange for your cat to be groomed and de-matted under sedation (and then resolve never to allow your pet to get into such a condition again).

WHILE GROOMING: -

Fleas

Check for any signs of fleas (see Chapter 5) and apply an insecticidal dusting powder or spray if necessary.

Mites

Check ears for waxy deposits that may indicate the presence of ear mites (see Chapter 5).

Eyes

Check eyes for any discharge. Tear staining can be a problem on white cats. Cut away any badly stained hair and wipe clean with Sherley's Eye Lotion.

Teeth

Check the mouth not only for bad teeth that may need attention but also for heavy tartar deposits that often form around the teeth (see Chapter 7 - Teeth). Regular scaling may be necessary in some cases to maintain a healthy mouth but, as a rule, this is best carried out by a Veterinary Surgeon and under sedation or general anaesthetic.

Nails

The nails of cats do not, as a rule, need regular trimming if the cat has the opportunity to get out and climb trees. However, in cases where they are inclined to tear at the furniture it may help to trim just the very tip of the nails with nail clippers. The nail contains a strong nerve and blood supply so it is important to understand that it is only the dead horny tip that is to be cut. If you feel uncertain about the amount to take off, ask your Veterinary Surgeon or animal welfare clinic to show you.

Tapeworms

The presence of tapeworms may sometimes be detected by dried-up segments, rather like grains of rice, adhering to the fur in the anal region (see Chapter 5).

BATHING

Cats tend to object to bathing even more than dogs and it is not, as a rule, necessary to bath them if grooming is carried out regularly, except in the case of show cats, or white cats (see later in this chapter). However, if bathed from kittenhood the procedure is far less troublesome.

Dry Cleaning

Cats can be "dry" cleaned by dusting a little Baby Talcum Powder into the coat and then thoroughly brushing out. Remember that powder left in the coat may lead to disqualification from cat shows.

Grooming will not be an ordeal if it is carried out at least weekly. After the more difficult work of brushing and combing take a little time to stroke your cat and tell him how handsome he looks. He will appreciate it.

PREPARING FOR A CAT SHOW

Good condition

The general advice given is this chapter on Cat Care applies to all pets but if a cat is to be entered for shows it is essential that its coat should be kept in good condition all year round. There can be no question of resorting to scissors to remove tangles, tangles must not be allowed to form. However, it is a pity to make a cat a house prisoner simply in the interest of his appearance and many breeders feel that cats which live in centrally heated homes really need the contact with the cold outside world to produce a thick and glossy coat.

For shorthaired cats follow the routine suggested earlier in the chapter and simply finish by polishing the coat by smoothing over (in the natural direction of the hair) with a soft duster or by using a grooming aid such as Sherley's Grooming Spray.

Longhaired cats require more attention and it is essential to be certain that the grooming is thorough and that no knots are left anywhere in the coat. Light-coloured coats may benefit from a bath and this is best carried out two to three days before a show.

Shampoo

Use lukewarm water and a special cat shampoo, e.g. one from the Sherley's Diagnos range. Be sure to rinse very thoroughly (a spray tap fitting is a great help) and see that the cat is kept in a warm, even temperature while drying. If the cat is fairly placid, use an electric hairdryer to bring up a fluffy coat. In the case of a longhaired cat, the final brushing out should be against the natural direction of the coat to produce a really fluffy effect.

SHOWING & BREEDING PEDIGREE CATS

There may be some extrovert felines who really enjoy showing off and being admired but the majority would probably say, if they could speak, that the glory of winning shows hardly compensates for all that they had to endure in washing, brushing, and combing beforehand. However, there is no doubt that the work of the Governing Council of the Cat Fancy (GCCF) and all its affiliated clubs in promoting shows has done a great deal for the welfare of cats in general and in increasing interest and concern for them among the general public.

REGISTRATION

There are often small local shows of a general nature where children can enjoy showing their pets but if cats are to be shown at any of the shows licensed by the GCCF, they must first be registered (unless they are shown in the Household Pet Class).

Cats may have two names. A prefix which is the "family name" or registered name of the breeder and an affix which is the name of the individual cat.

There is a charge for the prefix registered for the life of the breeder with the GCCF. In addition, charges are made for each kitten or cat registered.

Information

Further information and registration forms may be obtained by sending a stamped, addressed envelope to The Governing Council of the Cat Fancy (the address of which can be found in the section entitled "Useful Contacts" at the end of this book). They will also supply the following that will be useful to the prospective cat shower:

Show list for the current year.

Club list.

Show rules.

It will be realised that over the years many of the more obvious names have been taken (and they cannot be re-used for twenty years) so it is wise to look for unusual names and to give a choice. Certain categories of names cannot be used and these are defined in the registration certificate application form, so it should be read through thoroughly before completing and returning.

Registration lasts throughout the life of the individual cat but if the cat is sold it cannot be shown until it is transferred to the new owner. The appropriate form can be obtained from the GCCF and a small charge will be made.

SHOWING

Anyone who is interested in showing or breeding cats would be wise to attend some shows in their own neighbourhood to decide which breed they would like to specialise in and try to form an idea in their own mind as to what constitutes a good specimen, as this is vital to their future success.

By attending cat shows the prospective owner will have the opportunity not only to acquire a judgement of the points of the show cat but also to meet and talk to breeders.

In this way it may be possible to find a kitten, or kittens that are required but alternatively the local paper will almost certainly carry advertisements from time to time. If you are prepared to go further afield, "Cats", the official newspaper of the GCCF, carries advertisements, official notices, and show reports from all over the country.

However, one should never make the mistake of buying a kitten unseen through an advertisement. Apart from the fact that on humane and practical grounds pet animals should never be sent by rail unescorted unless absolutely unavoidable, the old saying "Buyer Beware" still applies. If your kitten does not match up to the advertisement or arrives in poor condition, you may find it difficult to obtain redress.

Finding out about shows

The GCCF can supply you with a list of cat shows and a copy of the show rules. Anyone wishing to participate in showing would be wise to study them. This also applies to more experienced exhibitors since they are under an obligation to be aware of changes to the rules.

Shows are of two main categories: -

Championship Shows - where challenge certificates are awarded. The winner of three of these certificates (awarded at different shows) becomes a champion.

Exemption and Sanction Shows - challenge certificates are not awarded at these shows but they give breeders and especially newcomers to the cat fancy the opportunity to compare their cats with others and judge their potential for future shows.

PREPARING FOR A CAT SHOW

The actual grooming and preparation has already been dealt with earlier in the chapter but it also goes without saying that if a cat is to be shown it must be in the peak of physical condition. There will be a veterinary examination before admittance to the show, and a slight discharge from the eyes or even the presence of one flea can cause disqualification.

Vaccination

Show cats should be vaccinated against feline enteritis and cat flu but vaccination should be carried out no later than three weeks prior to the show.

Feeding

If the cat is going to the show in the morning it may be given a small meal first thing. A container of water should be provided plus a litter tray.

Travelling

It is essential to have a strong roomy cat box and also one that can be easily and quickly opened to avoid delays at the veterinary inspection. Your cat should be accustomed in advance to travelling and to spending several hours in a confined space. It is also important that it should be quite used to being handled by strangers, since a cat that cannot be taken out of its cage will be disqualified.

ADMISSION

Admission and "vetting" usually starts anytime between 7:30 and 10:00 am in the morning, although in some cases cats may be admitted the previous evening and housed overnight. They must arrive in a proper box and not be brought on lead and harness, or carried in.

Pen

During the show the cat must be confined to its appropriate pen. You will have been given a tally number with your cat, on admission, and the cage will have the corresponding number.

Cats are not lead or held for showing, as is the case at dog shows. The judge(s) will make the rounds and then the cat will be lifted onto a table and judged.

Cat shows usually finish around 6:00 pm, but owners are allowed to feed their cats during the afternoon if they wish.

Showing cats cannot be considered a profitable proposition in any way. The cash prizes are usually quite small and often replaced by rosettes, and the time and travel which is involved as well as the entry fees, usually leaves the exhibitor well out of pocket. However, as a hobby it obviously holds a great fascination for cat lovers and, for the serious cat breeder, showing adds prestige and value to their kittens.

Cat clubs

In most areas there are cat clubs devoted to various breeds, Siamese, Burmese, Abysinnian, and so on. These clubs hold shows locally under the jurisdiction of the National Cat Club. There are two main large shows of the year; the huge National Cat Club Show at London Olympia and the Supreme Cat Show at the NEC Birmingham.

BREEDING PEDIGREE CATS FOR SHOW & SALE

Do not go into cat breeding with the idea of making money. It can sometimes be profitable if you have several healthy litters in turn but feeding and veterinary charges, together with the cost of attending shows, makes it more likely that you will operate at a loss. It is much safer to regard it as a hobby to be enjoyed for its own sake.

Choose one, or if you wish, two healthy female kittens, either at eight weeks, or nearer breeding age at nine months to one year. However, do realise that you will have to pay more for an older female (queen) which appears to have show potential or which has already been shown successfully.

Do not make the mistake of buying a male and a female. This causes considerable difficulties once the female comes into season if you do not wish to breed at once.

KEEPING A STUD CAT

Whilst this may be quite profitable it is not always easy. An unneutered male, if allowed freedom, will range abroad constantly in search of females and will usually become scarred and battered as a result of fighting. On the other hand, a tom is not an ideal house cat and if it is deliberately kept in may start to urinate or spray in the home, especially in the breeding season, and the resulting smell is both persistent and unpleasant.

Ideally a stud cat should be kept in an outdoor pen which has an exercise area and an inner pen that can be heated. This should be reasonably large so that visiting females can be introduced for mating when necessary.

MATING

As a rule no assistance is needed, although the cats should be supervised to avoid injuries and to be certain that mating has taken place. They may mate several times within the space of a few hours and since ovulation appears to occur as a response to mating, pregnancy usually follows. Most owners of stud toms now insist that before your cat is allowed on the premises it is tested and certified negative for Feline Leukaemia Virus (see Chapter 7).

In cases where mating proves unsuccessful, the owner of the tom may allow a second mating without charge but this should be ascertained in advance, as it is not an invariable rule. In many cases it may be possible to leave a queen for a day or two if she is rather unsettled at first, to be certain of a satisfactory mating.

CARE OF THE FEMALE

Season

As we have said in Chapter 2, cats usually start to come into oestrus or season at seven to eight months and if mated at this time will become pregnant. However, it is not wise to start breeding intentionally much before one year, to allow the cat to finish growing and reach maturity.

A cat in season can cause considerable problems. The female in oestrus is quite determined to get out and will miaow loudly and persistently, especially the Siamese. If she should get out she will certainly be mated by a neighbouring tomcat and produce a litter of cross-breds. This will not, as some people suppose, "spoil" the cat for future pedigree breeding, but it will obviously waste a certain amount of time. However, while crossbred kittens from Siamese, or other pedigree females do not usually have the typical coloration of the parent, they do inherit many of the breed characteristics and readily find homes as pets as a rule.

It is possible to postpone the onset of oestrus by means of an injection (usually for a period of about six months) or tablets. If the problem of keeping a female confined to the house proves particularly difficult in your individual circumstances, it is worth discussing this type of treatment with your Veterinary Surgeon.

Before the time arrives when you wish to have your cat mated try to get in touch with the owner of a suitable stud cat in your area. For information concerning cats at stud contact the applicable Breed Club. A list of Affiliated Clubs is available from the GCCF (see 'Useful Addresses' at the back of this book).

Pregnancy

The advice given on diets and general care in pregnancy in Chapter 2 applies equally to pedigree cats. However, pedigree cats are often more nervous and highly strung and extra care may be required at the time of the birth.

Prepare a cardboard box with a warm (not hot) hot water bottle covered with a soft blanket. If the mother cat becomes agitated during the birth of the kittens, any that have arrived can be removed to safety and kept in a warm place, to be returned as soon as she becomes calmer.

Cord

In some instances, if the mother cat is nervous and upset and does not bite through the umbilical cord, it may be necessary for the owner to ligate it (see Chapter 2 - Cutting the Cord).

VETERINARY HELP

It may be a wise precaution to advise your own Veterinary Surgeon of the expected arrival of the kittens and to find out what arrangements he makes for emergency calls after hours if it should become necessary.

REARING & WEANING KITTENS - See Chapter 3

Finally, do obtain pedigree forms well in advance and have them made out before advertising the kittens for sale.

TRAVEL & HOLIDAYS

Alternatives

Holiday time may present a problem to the cat owner. The alternatives are, as a rule, either putting the cat into a cattery or leaving him at home to be cared for by a neighbour. There may be a third solution in taking your cat with you. This may sound impractical but cats are becoming more sophisticated today and it is not uncommon to hear of owners who take their cats away with them, even on caravan holidays. However, this is a habit that should be started young and it would not be wise to attempt it with a middle-aged or nervous cat. If a cat is to travel with you it is important to get him accustomed to wearing a harness or a collar and lead in early life.

LEAVING THE CAT AT HOME

If you have anyone who will stay in the house this is ideal. Cats are very attached to places and if they are left in their own homes and given their usual meals it seems that they do not miss their owners too much. If, however, the cat is left at home, with a neighbour coming in to feed him, or shut him in at night the situation is less happy. There is always the chance that your pet might become involved in an accident and no-one would know. Alternatively, he might become ill and involve the friend or neighbour in unexpected difficulties. For these reasons, always ensure that your neighbour knows how to contact you and has the name of your Veterinary Surgeon.

Catteries

Catteries are there to care for your cat when you are away and when there is nobody else to look after the cat at home.

The majority of cats settle well, but occasionally seem to miss their "home comforts", but in general little harm will come of this.

Due to the possible disease risks when lots of cats are brought together under one roof most catteries will, quite rightly, insist on all cats being vaccinated against flu and enteritis before being admitted.

CAT FLU & FELINE ENTERITIS

Cat flu and feline enteritis are two very serious, and often fatal, viral diseases of cats. They can be prevented very successfully by vaccination. See that your young kitten is vaccinated and remember that booster injections are necessary, especially before sending your pet into a boarding cattery. Your own Veterinary Surgeon will advise you.

Young cats settle better in catteries than older ones, so if it is going to be necessary to leave your pet from time to time, try to establish the habit early and accustom him to the occasional absence from home.

CHOOSING A CATTERY

Check
yourself

This can be difficult if you are new to the area. Personal recommendation by another cat owner helps, but failing this select a kennel or cattery from the local newspaper, Yellow Pages, or the telephone directory. Well before your holiday is due, visit and satisfy yourself that the place is clean, secure, and well run. Don't leave things until the last minute when it is too late to change your mind.

THINGS TO LOOK FOR WHEN CHOOSING A CATTERY: -

Cages should be clean, large enough for comfort, and well ventilated.

Warmth - heated catteries are essential in winter and owners must be prepared to pay for the extra costs. Cats that are used to living in centrally heated houses suffer considerably if they are put in unheated cages.

Exercise runs - if there is not an exercise run attached to each cage there should be an exercise area where the cat can be put out each day.

There should be someone living on the premises by night as well as by day in case of fire. Above all, the proprietor should be a person who really cares and understands cats. Without this, the most modern and efficient cattery will not be a success.

Book well ahead - good catteries may become fully booked in the holiday season.

Licensed kennels and catteries are inspected and licensed by the local authorities, so if you really feel that a particular cattery was dirty or gave unsatisfactory care it is worth reporting.

Vaccination certificates are usually required, so check with your Veterinary Surgeon if your cat is due for a booster injection.

Ask if you may take your cat's own bed - it will smell like home and may help him feel less homesick.

Food - ask if your cat may have the food he is used to - or take a supply in for him.

Weight - don't blame the cattery owner if your cat has lost weight when you collect him. It is most unlikely that he has been short of food but unfortunately some cats fret in catteries and refuse to eat. In these cases it is kinder to make arrangements for the cat to stay in his own home if he has been particularly unhappy.

No real cat lover will enjoy a holiday knowing that his or her pet is unhappy or neglected.

Transport - always use a strong and reliable cat box or basket when transporting your cat. A frightened cat will often struggle to get out - and nothing could be worse than losing your cat in a strange place.

TYPES OF BASKET

Traditional wicker cat baskets are satisfactory as long as the fastenings remain secure. They have the advantage that they are made of natural fibre and have good ventilation but they are difficult to disinfect if it should become necessary following an infectious illness.

Ventilation

Fibre-glass boxes are strong and can be washed out easily and disinfected but it is important to be certain that the ventilation holes are adequate, especially for larger cats, if they are to be kept in them for any length of time.

Wire mesh or metal cages are strong and provide ample ventilation but because they are so open they provide no sense of security to the cat if a strange person (or dog) should approach. There are also a wide variety of plastic cat homes available.

For those cats that travel infrequently, or for short journeys, the cardboard cat boxes sold by the various welfare organisations are useful. But be warned, they will not hold a large and frightened cat!

TRAVEL BY SEA, RAIL, & AIR

If possible travel with your pet. In a train you will, as a rule, be allowed to keep a cat in the carriage providing he is in a proper cat box or basket.

It is a sensible plan to line the base of the basket with a sheet of polythene, covered by several layers of newspaper, in case of unexpected accidents.

TRAVELLING UNACCOMPANIED

Strong box

If it is absolutely necessary to send a cat by train unaccompanied, choose a passenger train and notify the recipient to be on the platform to meet it. Use a strong wooden box, which is secure but with adequate ventilation. Line the box with several layers of newspaper and add a blanket for comfort and warmth. See that the box is marked "Live Cat" or "Kitten" and that the address of the sender and recipient are quite clearly visible. Unfortunately, even with the most careful arrangements, delays and misdirections occur, but in this way you can be told whether the cat has reached his destination safely. If you have to send a cat by train unaccompanied, it would be wise to contact your local Station Master and clarify the position.

Car

Although the first car journey may prove rather alarming, many cats become quite seasoned car travellers. However, it is essential for driver safety that they should be confined to a basket during the journey.

Sea or air

If it is necessary to send a cat unaccompanied by sea or air it is best to consult one of the firms which specialise in this work. They will be able to provide a secure and suitable box and will advise you of the regulations governing travel.

WHEN TAKING YOUR CAT ABROAD

When taking your cat out of the United Kingdom you will require a certificate of health given by a Veterinary Surgeon within a few days of leaving.

Rabies

In addition, some countries require your cat to be vaccinated against rabies, or require you to produce a certificate showing that your pet is free from diseases. In some countries there is a short quarantine period on arrival, but because the United Kingdom is free from rabies most places will admit British cats at once. It really is important to find out all these details about the country concerned as soon as possible. Your Veterinary Surgeon will often be able to help you find out what is required. Failure to do this may involve you in considerable delay, or heartbreak, if you find that you are unable to take your pet with you.

QUARANTINE REGULATIONS

UK quarantine regulations have now been phased out. In place is the "Pet Travel Scheme" which enables cats and dogs coming from European Union Countries, and other countries which are part of the scheme, to enter the UK without quarantine. The system will also cover UK resident cats and dogs that have been abroad temporarily in those countries. Pets from countries which are not part of the scheme will continue to be subject to quarantine.

For further information on UK quarantine and the new regulations contact the Department for Environment, Food and Rural Affairs (or if in Scotland the Department of Agriculture and Fisheries for Scotland).

CARING FOR THE ELDERLY CAT

With better feeding and medical care the family cat is becoming very long lived. Ages of sixteen and seventeen are by no means uncommon and with very little extra care and attention old age can be a very pleasant and contented time.

Feeding

Proprietary canned cat foods may still be given and they are particularly suitable for those elderly cats who have lost some or all of their teeth. However, elderly appetites can be capricious and the time for indulgence has arrived, so it may be advisable to try fresh foods such as rabbit, fish, or mince from time to time to maintain a high protein level and add interest to the diet.

Diets

In cases where specific illness has been diagnosed (such as kidney disease) your own Veterinary Surgeon will advise you as to the foods which are most suitable for your pet, and will probably supply you with a specifically prepared prescription diet.

Warmth

Adequate rest and warm surroundings are of great importance in the case of the elderly cat. In winter particularly, old cats may seem to sleep for almost all of 24 hours, if they can find a cosy place in an airing cupboard or near a radiator, and in the summer they will select the sunniest spots in the garden for dozing. However, in spite of this they will suddenly surprise you by playing like a kitten with a toy or a piece of string.

Medical care

A regular visit to your Veterinary Surgeon or Animal Welfare Clinic, perhaps once a year, or every six months, is a wise precaution to be certain that your pet is still well enough to enjoy life.

TROUBLES OF OLD AGE

Teeth

Teeth can be a common cause of discomfort and loss of appetite. If your Veterinary Surgeon advises extractions you will find, as a rule, that it produces a great improvement in general well being. Hard healthy gums are of much more use for eating than bad teeth.

Nails

As the joints become stiffer, cats may be unable to sharpen their own claws and may have difficulty in retracting them when they become caught in cloth. Regular trimming of the overgrown tips of the nails will help minimise this problem.

Constipation

Some elderly cats suffer from a severe type of constipation, largely as a result of loss of muscle tone in the bowel, although it may also be due to the lack of proper exercise, or to swallowing

large quantities of hair in the moulting season.

Including liver in the diet (raw or cooked) once or twice weekly will usually have a natural laxative effect. Sherley's Cat-a-Med Hairball Remover may be given to assist the passage of fur balls.

If these first aid measures prove ineffective it is best to consult a Veterinary Surgeon for further advice.

Incontinence

Unfortunately, some elderly cats may lose control of their bladder and bowels and however much you love your pet this can make life very difficult. It is, of course, useless and unkind to blame the animals; this is something they cannot help. Consult your Veterinary Surgeon who will tell you if any medical help can be given, or if you can expect any improvement in the condition.

EUTHANASIA

In cases where a cat is suffering from a painful and incurable condition, or when your Veterinary Surgeon advises that life cannot be prolonged with kindness, euthanasia should be considered (see Chapter 7).

INTERNAL & EXTERNAL PARASITES

INTERNAL PARASITES

WORMS

It sometimes comes as quite a shock to an owner to discover that his much loved pet is the host to quite a number of parasites, and the sight of a flea, or worse still a tapeworm segment, in an otherwise spotless home can be disturbing. However, modern preventative measures for these pests are simple and effective and, with reasonable care, parasites should not be a problem.

THE RISK TO YOUR PET

The major internal parasites of the cat in this country are not bloodsuckers but feed on microscopic particles of semi-digested food within the gut. In spite of this, large numbers of the parasites in the stomach or the lumen of the bowel can interfere with digestion and lead to poor condition in the adult, while in the young kitten the presence of worms and their larval forms in the body can constitute a real danger to life.

ROUNDWORM

Toxocara cati:

Appearance   Similar to a thin garden worm, these may be up to several inches in length and are sometimes coiled in a mass. Their colour is whitish or pinkish brown, owing to ingested food material.

The adult worm may be passed in the faeces but because of the cat's cleaning habits the worms are not as easily detected in cats as in dogs. They may also be vomited and it is not uncommon for an adult cat to expel a single large worm when regurgitating hair.

Recognition

Worm eggs ingested by the cat, hatch out as larvae in the intestines, pass through the gut wall, and migrate for a period in the body before returning to the intestine. Some of the larvae fail to return to the intestine and become dormant in the tissues of the cat.

Life cycle

Dormant larvae of the worm can also be found in tissues of other creatures, e.g. mice that have eaten eggs. If, for example, a mouse containing larvae in its tissues is eaten, these larvae develop into adult worms in the cat's intestine.

Young kittens can be infected either by ingesting eggs or by ingesting larvae that are passed through the mother's milk.

Roundworms

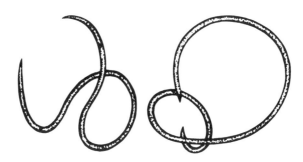

Toxascaris leonina:

This is not a common roundworm in the cat. The main route of infection is by ingestion of dormant larvae in the tissues of prey such as mice.

Danger to very young

Young kittens may show quite severe symptoms of poor growth, loss of appetite, and abdominal distension as a result of adult worms in the intestines. They may also suffer from the presence of the larval form of the worm that migrates through the liver and lungs.

Do not dose

While a kitten affected by heavy roundworm infestation may show the symptoms described above, it is a mistake for an owner to assume that worms are the cause of all illnesses in young kittens. Similar symptoms might well indicate the onset of a viral disease and while modern worm remedies are very safe for the normal cat, they should not be given to a cat that seems unwell unless the diagnosis is certain or without first checking with a Veterinary Surgeon.

Treatment

Starving before treatment is not necessary nowadays. Modern worm treatments are not in any way distressing to the patient and they are safe and effective in the normal healthy cat. Sherley's produce a range of treatments for roundworm, including granules, tablets, liquid, and cream.

Administration

Tablets (which can be finely powdered between two sheets of paper) or liquid medicine can usually be given with the food. However, a very light knowledge of the cat psychology will tell you that many cats are extremely suspicious of anything unusual in their meal. This can best be overcome by mixing the medicine with a favourite and strongly flavoured food and by making certain that the cat is really hungry beforehand. Alternatively, granules are a much easier way to worm. They are virtually tasteless and odourless, and are simply sprinkled over the cat's food for trouble-free routine worming.

If your cat is really resistant to any foreign substance in the food, administer the medicine on its own following a small meal (see Chapter 6 for advice on this).

Only the worms that are in the intestines are susceptible to the wormer and so repeated dosing is needed to ensure that your cat's worm burden is kept to a minimum.

Frequency of dosing

A suggested regime is given below: -

Age	Dose
2 weeks until 12 weeks	Every 2 weeks with a roundworm treatment
12 weeks until 24 weeks	Every 4 weeks with a roundworm treatment
24 weeks (6 months) onwards	4 times a year with a roundworm/tapeworm treatment

Risk to man

Much has been written during the recent years of the risk of passing worm infection from pets to man and, whilst this should not be minimised or overlooked, it should be kept in perspective. Cat tapeworm have (extremely rarely) been found in man but this is an unlikely risk since the tapeworm is transmitted through an intermediate host (a mouse or a flea) and it is only by swallowing an infected host that man could acquire the worm.

Visceral larval migrans

Extremely rarely, roundworms can cause a serious condition (visceral larval migrans) in children who have become infected with the migrating larvae of the worm as a result of swallowing the eggs. Although the incidence is rare, it is worth remembering that a simple worming regime can prevent this so very easily.

TAPEWORM

Tapeworms are more commonly found as parasites in the adult cat rather than young kittens.

One of the most common tapeworms of the cat is Dipylidium caninum. The flea acts as the intermediate host of this tapeworm and a cat acquires the worm by swallowing an infected flea whilst grooming. Thus effective flea control also plays a very important part in the control of this worm.

Tapeworm (showing the head on the left)

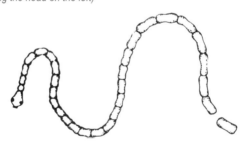

Another common tapeworm, especially found in hunting cats, belongs to the Taenia family of worms. These are acquired by ingesting intermediate hosts such as mice, rats, birds and rabbits.

Recognition

Tapeworms consist of a line of individual segments that are linked together, rather like a train, which terminate at the narrow end of the head (the scolex) armed with hooks and suckers which are used to attach the worm to the lining of the intestine. The worm may be up to fifteen feet in length, yellowish white in appearance and it is not unusual for a cat to harbour several at one time.

What to look for

The presence of the tapeworm is usually recognised when the mature segments start to be shed via the rectum, or with the faeces, or occasionally when the cat vomits a complete worm. Dipylidium segments are about an eighth of an inch in length, oval in shape and, when they are shed, may be capable of some movement. The dried-up segments may also be found sticking to the hair in the anal region and resemble grains of rice. Because of their appearance owners sometimes mistakenly assume that they are roundworms. It is only the complete worm that has the typical "tape" appearance that gives it its name. To treat your cat effectively it is wise to identify the type of parasite, or choose a wormer that kills both types of worm.

Do not usually make cats thin

The actual amount of food that is consumed by tapeworms is so small that it is of no consequence, and it is only when the worms are present in very large quantities that they may interfere with normal digestion. If your cat starts to lose weight, never assume that worms are the cause without first checking with your Veterinary Surgeon. However, the presence of worms almost certainly causes some discomfort or irritation to the cat and the shedding of the segments in the house is aesthetically very unpleasant. If you have definite proof of the presence of worms you should carry out treatment to eliminate these parasites for the good of all concerned.

How they are spread

Tapeworms are never spread directly from cat to cat but, as mentioned earlier, require an intermediate host to complete their complicated life cycle. These may be mice, rabbits, birds, or fleas.

When the cat passes the mature segments of the tapeworm they contain many thousands of microscopic eggs. The segments dry out and rupture, liberating the eggs either into the soil where they are swallowed by rabbits or mice, or into the animal's hair or the bedding where they are swallowed by fleas. Within the intermediate host the eggs of the worm hatch out to form larvae, and when the mouse or flea is eaten by the cat the cycle is completed and the larvae develop into new tapeworms in the gut of their new host.

The intermediate host

As you can see, in the case of the Dipylidium tapeworm, eliminating the mature worm is only half the battle. It is necessary where possible to eliminate, as well, the intermediate host, the flea, which provides a constant source of reinfection.

Hunting cats

Many cats are inveterate hunters and in country areas they may well quite regularly kill and eat young rabbits. They also kill mice and we are usually quite glad to let them do so. In this situation it is best to carry out a routine of regular treatment with a Taenia tapeworm remedy.

OTHER WORMS

Lungworm

The lungworm (Aleurostrongylus) causes respiratory symptoms and pneumonia but it is uncommon and not readily diagnosed by an owner.

Hookworm

The hookworm is a true blood-sucking worm (Uncinaria) and, if present in large quantities, can lead to debility and anaemia. However, it is not very common in domestic pets in the UK. The worm is very tiny (about half an inch long) and is not readily recognised. If you suspect that your cat may be infected it is best to consult a Veterinary Surgeon for a definite diagnosis.

EXTERNAL PARASITES

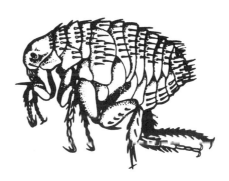

Typical flea
Cats can harbour quite a number of external parasites. Fortunately, very few of these parasites will cause any problem to the owners but they can cause significant clinical problems in the cat. The flea is the most common of the external parasites of the cat and this will be dealt with in som detail.

Fleas are wingless insects of which there are approximately 2,000 species, sixty of which are in the UK. Fortunately for us, only a few species are found on dogs and cats. The most common or being, in fact, the cat flea (Ctenocephalides felis). Other species occasionally found include the dog flea, hedgehog flea, rabbit flea, and (rarely) the human flea.

Like all insects, they progress through a cycle of egg - larva - pupa - and finally the adult.

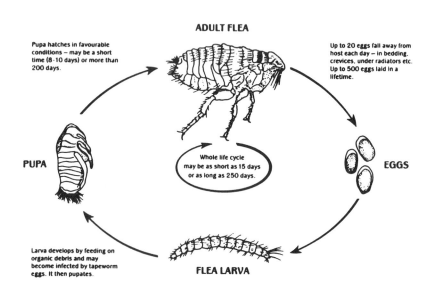

ADULT FLEA

Pupa hatches in favourable conditions – may be a short time (8-10 days) or more than 200 days.

Up to 20 eggs fall away from host each day – in bedding. crevices, under radiators etc. Up to 500 eggs laid in a lifetime.

PUPA

Whole life cycle may be as short as 15 days or as long as 250 days.

EGGS

Larva develops by feeding on organic debris and may become infected by tapeworm eggs. It then pupates.

FLEA LARVA

The life cycle of the flea

Adult

Adult fleas are brown and about two to three millimetres in length. They are very thin to allow eas passage through the coat of the animal. They spend the majority of their life on the host animal and it is only when very close contact occurs between animals, e.g. sleeping together, will a sma number of adult fleas cross to an uninfected animal.

They feed several times a day by sucking blood from the host animal with their specially adapted mouthparts. Some animals and humans develop a hypersensitivity to flea saliva and this can cause a very itchy reaction at the site of the flea bite.

The female flea is a most prolific egg producer and on average produces up to thirty eggs per da During her life, she can produce four to five hundred eggs in total. These eggs fall to the floor, usually wherever the cat walks and sleeps. Naturally, the highest number of eggs will be where the animal spends most of its time - in its bedding, on the settee, or even on the bed! The eggs hatch into larvae (see diagram) which graze around the environment eating organic debris, including the dried faeces, or flea dirt, from adult fleas which essentially consists of dried blood, a good source of protein. The larvae then develop into pupae, from which adult fleas develop. The adult hatches from the pupa in response to stimulation, e.g. warmth and vibration, and immediately starts to look for a new host to begin the life cycle again.

This whole life cycle can take as little as two weeks under ideal conditions of warmth and humidity, but may extend to as long as a year when the climate is colder.

Incidence

In general, fleas start to breed in the spring. This leads to a gradual increase over the summer months to reach a peak in August and September. The numbers then start to decline with the colder weather, although central heating in many modern homes can help maintain a steady population of fleas throughout the winter.

Symptoms

A low number of fleas can exist on an animal without clinical signs being seen. Flea "dirt" (which is faecal material of the flea consisting almost entirely of dried blood) may be seen in the coat. A sure way to test whether your animal has fleas is to brush the coat the wrong way, allowing debris from the coat to fall onto moist tissue or blotting paper. Any dried specks of flea dirt will very soon start to dissolve producing a red ring on the paper.

More severe infestations will irritate the animal causing persistent scratching and nibbling at the fur, particularly around the base of the tail.

Occasionally, if your cat has gone out into the garden and encountered a rabbit or a hedgehog, you may see groups of fleas clustered in large numbers around the edges of the cat's ears or nose. This may be alarming, but these fleas will not breed on your cat, and will usually drop off to try and find their usual host.

Miliary eczema

Certain cats become hypersensitive and allergic to flea bites and this causes a particularly itchy and scabby dermatitis which is seen most easily along the back of cats.

Tapeworm

Fleas are the intermediate host of the Dipylidium tapeworm, so always de-worm your cat following a flea infestation.

Treatment and control

The treatment and control of fleas has two elements; the treatment of fleas on the animal, and the treatment of the environment. It is essential that both elements are carried out for successful control.

Animal treatment

Mechanical removal:
Fine tooth combs have been used for many years and whilst they can remove fleas, it is a laborious task and not completely effective.

Insecticides
Many products are on the market which are effective at killing fleas. Some also have a degree of persistency within the coat.

Application of insecticides can either be by aerosols, quiet pump-action sprays, or the use of insecticidal powders that are puffed or brushed into the coat.

Flea collars are also another way of applying an insecticide to cats (see later).

Environmental treatment

As the preceding diagram shows, a large proportion of the life cycle of the flea is spent in the environment. The most common failing, when trying to control fleas is to treat the animal and ignore the environment. Neglecting this will result in a re-infestation from newly hatched fleas.

Mechanical removal of eggs, larvae, and pupae can be achieved to a certain extent by regular vacuum cleaning of all accessible areas where the cat sleeps. Regular washing of the pet's bedding also helps in this respect.

However, there are areas which are inaccessible, or which are not very easily cleaned, and further methods need to be used. One of the most common ways of achieving this is to use a residual insecticide, such as Sherley's Defest II, which will last for a period of up to twelve weeks after application. Defest II is applied to difficult to clean areas such as the skirting boards, under settees, chairs, etc. Any adult fleas or larvae hatching out encountering the insecticide will be killed. Thus the life cycle will be broken. It also has the added advantage of killing other unwanted insects such as ants, silverfish, and so on.

A modern alternative to Defest II is Flea Buster. Flea Buster is a non-insecticidal flea control product that works by dehydration. You simply sprinkle the powder on the carpet, brush in, and the effect will last for anything up to one year.

As mentioned above, the "flea season" builds up to a peak in August/September. The vast majority of these flea infestations arise as a result of fleas breeding in the house. By following the regime below, it should be possible to minimise the problems of this perennial pest: -

Prevention is better than cure

1. Regular vacuum cleaning and washing of pet bedding.
2. Treatment of inaccessible and difficult to clean areas with an environmental spray, such as Sherley's Defest II, at regular intervals according to manufacturers instructions. If this is carried out at the beginning of the year, the build up of fleas can be prevented.
3. Flea collars can be used which slowly release the active ingredient over a period of time. They work best by preventing flea infestations developing on the cat and it is therefore preferable to put one on when the animal is free of fleas. If your cat has the collar put on early in the year, this will help control the fleas that are encountered both in and outside the house. A Sherley's Lost & Found Flea Collar will also give the added bonus of your cat being registered and traceable, as well as killing fleas.

What to do if there is an outbreak

This is a question that is often asked, and the following steps will help to rapidly improve the situation: -

1. All cats and dogs in the household should be treated with an effective insecticide preparation (spray or powder).
2. All pet bedding should be thoroughly washed or destroyed.
3. Thorough vacuum cleaning of the house/kennels followed by an insecticidal residual spray such as Sherley's Defest II to kill adult fleas and their larvae.

This will resolve the situation in the majority of cases. However, very rarely, massive house infestations occur and the only recourse is to call the Environmental Health Office to fumigate the house.

Sherley's range of flea products

Sherley's manufacture an entire range of flea sprays, powders, and collars suitable for cats, and Sherley's Defest II, Flea Buster, Flego or Rug-de-Bug to treat the environment. Your pet shop will be able to supply you with the most appropriate preparation.

Sherley's also offer a "Flea Free Guarantee" service. This involves carrying out a four-step plan which, if carried out properly, guarantees to rid your home of fleas, or the money you spent on the products will be refunded. Contact your local pet shop or Sherley's direct for further information.

LICE

Recognition

Lice are not a common parasite of cats. They are mainly seen in young animals although older debilitated cats may also be affected.

They are very small and pinkish-white in colour. All of the life cycle is spent on the cat and their eggs (or "nits") stick to the hairs and may be seen with a magnifying glass.

Symptoms

Clinical signs are not always seen, but if present they cause similar signs to fleas, e.g. persistent scratching with some hair loss.

Treatment   Treatment with an insecticide on several occasions is needed to clear the infestation as only the adult stages are killed. You should consult your Veterinary Surgeon for suitable products.

Typical louse

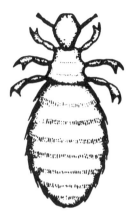

All in-contact animals should also be treated and the bedding washed, and clipping the coat may be required if the hair has become heavily matted.

TICKS

Ticks are not a normal parasite of the cat, but they are sometimes encountered in moorland areas.

Ticks are also sometimes found on hedgehogs, and this may be a source of infection in towns.

Recognition   Ticks are bluish-black in colour and rather like a small bean in appearance. They vary in size but after feeding on the host they become engorged with blood and may grow up to half an inch in length. At this stage they are sometimes mistaken for skin cysts but examination under a magnifying glass will reveal the presence of legs and biting mouthparts near the cat's skin.

Common tick

Treatment
Once ticks have finished feeding they will detach themselves and fall off. However, they can cause irritation to the cat and carry other diseases and so it is important to treat them as soon as they are seen, although this can be quite difficult.

When individual ticks are found they can be removed with tweezers after first soaking them with surgical spirit or coating them in Vaseline to cause withdrawal of the biting head. Alternatively, you can use Sherley's Tick Away, an easy-to-use spray for simple removal of ticks from your cat.

If the head is broken off it may result in a septic wound requiring veterinary treatment, so great care is needed.

Prevention
Insecticidal collars may help in prevention but regular grooming and inspection is the best method of control.

HARVEST MITES (Neotrombicula autumnalis)

Harvest mites can cause severe irritation and annoyance to pets and humans in the last of the summer months.

Recognition
The mites can just be seen with the naked eye as bright orange specks around the feet and legs and occasionally on the ear.

Treatment
Treatment is by application of an insecticide that readily kills the mite. However, occasionally, the irritation is so severe that veterinary attention may be needed.

CHEYLETIELLA

This is an uncommon mite infestation of cats. The entire life cycle is spent on the host and clinical signs can vary from mild to severe irritation with marked scurfiness of the coat.

Treatment
An insecticidal wash at weekly intervals is the best method of treatment. Consult your Veterinary Surgeon for suitable products.

All in-contact animals should also be treated and bedding washed.

THE EAR MITE (Otodectes)

The ear mite is one of the most troublesome external parasites of the cat. It is found living inside the ear canal, a place which even the most determined cat is unable to reach in grooming. It is almost invisible to the naked eye but may readily be seen with a magnifying glass. Large number of mites give a greyish crusty appearance to the inside of the ear. They are not bloodsuckers but live on particles of wax or exudate from the ear.

Recognition
Young cats pick up the mites from their mothers and are often severely infected. The presence of ear mites in the ear causes irritation and as a result excessive amounts of wax are formed which cause concrete-like encrustations in the ear. The constant scratching of the kitten causes exudation in the ear and bacterial infection may follow.

In older cats the first symptom to be noticed is often a bare or bleeding patch on the back of the ear. This is caused as a result of the cat's continuous scratching to try and get at the source of the irritation. Unfortunately, it is sometimes mistaken for the results of a cat fight by owners who treat the wound on the outside of the ear (with little success) without realising that the cause lies withi

Trans-
mission
Ear mites are not infectious to humans but they are very easily transmitted to other cats or to dogs.

Treatment

If the diagnosis is certain, relief from this can be quickly obtained by the application of eardrops designed to destroy the mite. Treatment should be repeated at weekly intervals to catch the new mites as they emerge from the eggs. However, if a bacterial infection is present a Veterinary Surgeon should be consulted.

Ear mite

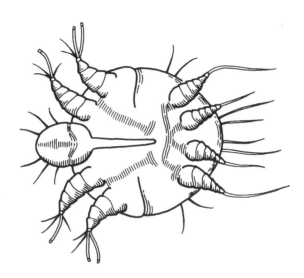

Where there are several encrustations of wax within the ear it may be necessary first to cleanse the ear canal before applying eardrops. To do this pour a few drops of a proprietary ear cleaner, such as Sherley's Ear Cleaner, into the ear, massage gently from the outside, then wipe away cleaner and wax with swabs of cotton wool. It is certainly not wise to use tweezers or any other sharp instrument to clean the ears, since a sudden movement from the cat may result in injury to the sensitive lining of the ear canal.

Warning

Ear mite infection is an extremely irritating condition. As soon as the cat's ear is touched it will trigger off an intense hind-leg scratch reflex, which may well result in the owner's hand being lacerated. For your own protection, before attempting any treatment, swathe the cat completely in a thick towel, or an old coat, right up to the neck, so that the feet are immobilised (see Chapter 6).

MANGE

Mites

The expression "a mangy cat" is sometimes heard but, in fact, mange (sarcoptic or demodectic) is hardly ever seen in the cat. The condition recognised by owners as mange is, as a rule, eczema - a non-infectious skin condition usually allergic in nature. See list of common ailments in Chapter 7.

The diagnosis of mange is made by demonstrating the presence of mites in a scraping taken from the superficial layers of the skin. If you suspect that your cat may have mange consult a Veterinary Surgeon.

NOTOEDRIC MANGE

This is, again, rarely seen. It affects the face and head of the cat and the irritation from the presence of the mite leads to self-inflicted bare or crusty areas. For treatment it is best to consult a Veterinary Surgeon.

RINGWORM

This extremely contagious skin condition is actually caused by a fungus.

Recognition

The typical ringworm lesion is a circular bare place with a crusty surrounding area which gradually increases in size, surrounded by broken hairs. However, any small bare patch, where there is loss of hair without any marked signs of soreness or irritation should be considered suspect and, in some cases, cats may be carriers of ringworm without showing any obvious lesions at all.

Transmission

It cannot be too strongly stressed that ringworm is extremely contagious not only to other animals but also to man, and more specifically, children, partly because their skin is more delicate but also because they spend more time in close contact with pets.

Cats pick up the infection from hedgehogs, rats and mice, but ringworm spores can remain active on woodwork or material for a very long time. The condition can spread very rapidly in a cattery due to direct and indirect contact.

Diagnosis

Always consult a Veterinary Surgeon at once if you suspect ringworm. He will be able to make a diagnosis by examining your cat under a Wood's Lamp (which causes the affected areas to fluoresce or glow in some cases) or by the microscopic examination of hair samples.

Treatment

Your Veterinary Surgeon may use tablets, shampoos, or combinations of these to treat the condition, and the treatment period may be prolonged.

MAGGOTS

These are not a true parasite of the cat but cats, like other animals, may sometimes be affected by them.

Maggots are produced from eggs of the common blowfly - just as meat is sometimes infected in the summer.

Recognition

The eggs are laid on an infected wound, or on soiled hair, and they are usually found on a cat that is already ill and weak, since healthy cats will not allow flies near them. They are most often seen on cats that have been injured and wandered away, especially during the summer months when flies are common.

THIS CONDITION IS EXTREMELY SERIOUS. The maggots feed on the cat's flesh and produce a toxic condition that is rapidly fatal.

Treatment

Consult a Veterinary Surgeon as soon as possible, but in the meantime cut away as much hair as possible from the area (it will probably be found to contain more of the tiny yellow eggs). Remove as many maggots as possible with tweezers and swab the area with a mild salt solution.

TREATMENT & FIRST AID IN ILLNESS

s he Ill or ot?

Sensible care and proper feeding will do a great deal to keep your cat fit, healthy, and active but accidents and illnesses can still occur. It is therefore important to know how to recognise the symptoms of ill health, how to deal with accidents and injuries, and to know when it is necessary to consult a Veterinary Surgeon.

It is true that cats are not always as easy to deal with as dogs but the average family cat is not a wild tiger and should not be treated as if he is. If the administration of tablets, of liquid medicines, or the treatment of wounds is approached in the right way it should not present problems. It is worth remembering that a cat which is well cared for, handled and groomed when he is well, will accept medical care much more readily when it becomes necessary.

HOW TO EXAMINE YOUR CAT

Some of this advice may sound obvious but it is surprising how often people overlook the simple rules of common sense and involve themselves in unnecessary difficulties. If your cat is placid and well behaved the advice may well be quite superfluous for you but if you know that your own pet is nervous, or have never tried to examine him before, it is best to take all necessary precautions.

Try to choose a room with a good natural or artificial light and check that doors and windows are securely fastened. Your cat may not wish to be examined and will make plans to leave as soon as he suspects your intentions.

Secure room	Try to choose a reasonably small room and one that is free from places where a cat can hide and not be retrieved easily (the spaces under cupboards and wardrobes for example). If necessary, block these exits off. Hours can be wasted in trying to coax a cross cat out of its retreat. If possible place the cat on a table as it is not easy to make a proper examination while crawling about on the floor.
Restraint	Immobilise the patient as far as possible. This is best done by placing him in the centre of a really thick blanket or old coat and wrapping it completely around. Leave only the head out if the head or mouth is to be examined, or leave space to look at an injury on a limb, or leave the tail free if the temperature is to be taken. Cats, if they are frightened or in pain, or if they resent treatment, will not hesitate to use their sharp claws and teeth to help them escape, so be warned that a small or thin blanket will not be sufficient.
Gloves	Some people may prefer to put on a thick pair of gardening gloves as a precautionary measure but these are rarely proof against bites and have the disadvantage of being rather clumsy when handling the cat.
Opening the mouth	To open the mouth, wrap the cat up as described above. If possible, get a friend to help by standing behind the cat, and holding firmly onto the blanket, restrain him from attempting to raise the front paws. Then place one hand firmly over the cat's head from behind, gripping at each side of the upper jaw and gently tip the head back to open the jaws. This may be sufficient to give a view of the inside of the mouth but it may also help to place the forefinger of the other hand on the point of the lower jaw to depress it slightly at the same time.

ADMINISTRATION OF TABLETS

Smooth-coated tablets usually present little problem. Open the mouth as described above and drop the tablet at the back of the cat's tongue (as centrally as possible) and quickly shut the mouth, allowing him to swallow.

Rough-coated tablets are inclined to stick and if they are bitter or unpleasant to taste the cat will fight against being given them again. This can be overcome by putting the tablet inside a piece of firm butter (or cheese can sometimes be used) and administering it in the same way.

While some modern medicines are almost tasteless and can be administered in food, there are still the exceptions. Even very hungry cats will, as a rule, examine their food before eating it and they are very quick to discover when any extraneous substances have been added.

LIQUID MEDICINES

These can be dealt within very much the same way but to avoid spills it is best to put the measured dose in a small bottle or an eyedropper. Wrap the cat up completely as before and open the mouth, tipping the head back slightly. Then trickle the liquid onto the cat's tongue, or behind the upper canine (fang) tooth, gently onto the hard palette, and you will find that in most cases it will swallow the medicine quite readily and without struggling.

RECOGNISING THE SYMPTOMS OF ILLNESS

Listlessness	Listlessness, disinclination to take food and a raised body temperature are the main signs of a generalised illness or infection.
Loss of appetite	Healthy cats will often sleep for hours and hours at a time and this is quite normal and typical of carnivore behaviour. However, an observant owner will readily detect the differences in the behaviour of a sick cat. It will remain in its own box or a quiet corner and will show no interest in its surroundings. It will not play, or react to its owner's voice, and it will not wash or stretch itself or rub affectionately against people's legs in the manner which is so typical of the cat which feels well

There are two main reasons for apparent loss of appetite. The cat may be unable to eat or it may feel ill and have no interest in eating.

Unwilling to eat

In the first case there is some physical reason why the cat cannot take its food. Typically, it will approach the plate eagerly and then turn away. This may indicate such conditions as a sore mouth, bad teeth or tooth abscesses in the older cat.

It may also be due to a foreign body in the mouth such as a bone lodged across the roof of the mouth, or at the side of the molar teeth, or a sewing needle lodged in the soft tissue.

Inappetence

In this case the cat is feeling ill or nauseous and shows no interest when food is offered, or simply turns the head away.

FIRST ELIMINATE OBVIOUS CAUSES

If your cat is a bird killer look for the telltale signs of feathers in the garden, or the over-distended stomach which may indicate that your cat has been eating between meals! This type of inappetence usually corrects itself quite quickly but if your cat has not recovered his appetite within 24 hours it may be wise to consult your Veterinary Surgeon.

If you can see no apparent reason for your cat's behaviour and he appears perfectly well and active, it is sensible to allow 24 hours to elapse before taking further advice. However, keep him under observation and do not offer alternative or tempting foods. It may well be that your pet has found something unwholesome to eat in a neighbour's rubbish bin and in this case starvation is the best policy.

However, if your cat refuses food and at the same time seems listless and quiet, he is probably ill. You should consult a Veterinary Surgeon as soon as possible.

Temperature

The temperature of the cat and other animals is usually taken in the rectum. The normal temperature of a healthy cat is 101.5°F (35-6°C) and a rise of even 1° may be a significant indication of illness.

Taking the temperature

Most cats resent having their temperature taken, so it is best to immobilise the patient in the manner described earlier by wrapping it in a thick blanket. If possible, get a friend to help but if this is not possible wrap the cat up, tuck it under one arm, or put it on a table and gently lean on it while holding onto the tail.

A heavy bulb Veterinary thermometer is easier to read and is slightly less easy to break. First shake the thermometer well so that the mercury falls in the tube. Lubricate the thermometer with Vaseline, insert the bulb into the rectum and wait for a specified time (usually one minute). Then withdraw the thermometer, wipe it on cotton wool and examine in a good light to read the level to which the mercury has risen. Always disinfect the thermometer before returning it to its case, using a chemical disinfectant (remember that a medical thermometer placed in boiling water will break).

Taking the pulse

The pulse can be detected by placing the hand inside the upper part of the hind leg, where the femoral pulse can be felt, but this is of little value to an unqualified person in assessing the state of health.

RECOGNISING SYMPTOMS OF PAIN

Cats that are in pain tend to resent handling and the first indication that an owner may notice is when a normally friendly cat growls or cries out on being lifted or stroked.

Strains and sprains

Muscular strains or sprains do occur in cats but they are less common than in dogs. Pain or swelling in a foot, limb, tail, or anywhere over the body surface is much more likely to be due to inflammation as a result of a small wound (usually a bite or a scratch). This usually leads to the formation of an abscess which not only causes acute local pain but may even result in a raised body temperature and general malaise (see Chapter 7).

Examination

If your cat appears to be in pain examine it carefully all over for any sign of swelling or hair loss, which may indicate the site or cause and then, of course, consult a Veterinary Surgeon (see next Chapter for advice on treatment).

Fractures (see later under "Accidents" in this chapter) are not always obvious or easy to diagnose. If your cat is quite unable to take any weight on a limb consult a Veterinary Surgeon as soon as possible.

Abdominal pain

The symptoms of abdominal (internal) pain are less easy to detect. However, a cat that is suffering from some severe abdominal condition will generally rest in an upright position, rather than curl up comfortably and it will sometimes give a rather harsh rasping purring sound.

RESPIRATION RATE

Danger signal

The actual rate at which a cat breathes is not of much assistance to an owner in judging the state of health. However, if the breathing becomes loud, rasping, or distressed, this is definitely a danger signal and may indicate such conditions as pneumonia, haemorrhage in the chest following an accident, or ruptured diaphragm. The cat will, as a rule, sit upright and will tend to raise the head in an attempt to breathe more easily.

Distressed breathing may also be associated with catarrhal conditions but signs of nasal discharge will usually indicate this.

VOMITING

Cats, like dogs, vomit very readily and this is, to some extent, a natural protective mechanism when they have eaten some irritant substance, or simply eaten too much.

Hairballs

Vomiting often expels hairballs in the stomach and this is especially noticeable in the moulting season.

Worms

Severe infestations of round or tapeworms may cause vomiting in cats or kittens.

However, if vomiting persists, it is almost certainly a symptom of illness and if not checked can lead very quickly to dehydration. Consult a Veterinary Surgeon as soon as possible.

THIRST

As we have said before cats do not, as a rule, drink very much and a sudden increase in thirst is almost always an indication of ill health. However, if a cat has changed from eating canned or fresh meat to a concentrated type of semi-moist or dried food this will be likely to cause a natural compensating increase in drinking.

RETCHING

By this is meant sudden and convulsive contractions of the muscles of the abdominal wall.

STRAINING

Constipation or diarrhoea can produce straining and it is, of course, important to be certain of the cause before attempting to treat the symptoms.

In the unneutered female straining may indicate the onset of birth pains.

BLADDER

Cystitis

An inflammation of the bladder will cause symptoms of straining (most often in the female). The cat will typically go to its litter tray and strain and may pass a few drops of urine or blood. However, these symptoms may also indicate a bladder obstruction as a result of calculi (bladder stones) in the urethra, which generally occurs in male cats. This condition is not only very painful but is extremely serious and may be fatal if help cannot be obtained quickly (see Feline Urethral Syndrome - Chapter 7).

TREATMENT FOR ACCIDENTS

This, of course, will depend greatly on the severity of the accident and it is not always easy for an inexperienced person to assess the degree of damage. As a general rule, keep the patient quiet and warm and contact a Veterinary Surgeon as soon as possible to arrange for an examination and whatever treatment is needed.

Should you move the patient?

As a general rule where accidents to humans are concerned the advice given is that the patient should not, on any account, be moved. Where cats are concerned this advice cannot be applied in quite the same way, although it should be stressed that if any injured animal has to be moved, it must be done as gently as possible, to avoid the risk of further displacement of broken bones.

If a cat is injured and lying on the road it must, of course, be moved to safety or there is every chance that it will be struck again by the next car.

There is also the risk that a cat lying by the roadside, apparently unconscious, will start to come round and will then panic and bolt, only to collapse in some place where it cannot be found or helped.

Fights

Unfortunately, even the smallest bite or scratch from another cat is liable to result in a painful abscess (see next chapter for advice on treatment). It is not unusual to find the claw of the adversary still embedded in the wound.

Dogs

Attacks by dogs probably occur less than one might think, although when they do occur they are likely to be serious. Dogs will often kill young kittens, simply because their instinct is to attack anything that runs away and if two dogs attack a cat the pack instinct to kill seems to assert itself. However, if an adult cat is chased by a dog it usually makes use of its ability to climb out of danger, or if it decides to stand its ground can often put the dog to flight.

Shock

Injured animals are usually in a state of shock and the best first aid measure that can be given is to see that they are kept warm. If the cat is in a basket, cover it with a light, warm blanket and place the basket near a radiator or, if this cannot be done, put a well-wrapped warm hot water bottle in the basket. Consult a Veterinary Surgeon without delay.

Fractures

It is not wise or helpful for an inexperienced person to attempt to splint a broken limb. The only practical treatment is to place the cat in a basket or in a strong box so that it can be lifted without any unnecessary movement of the damaged leg and to contact a Veterinary Surgeon as soon as possible (see also Chapter 7).

Haemorrhage

Superficial arterial haemorrhage is fortunately much less common in the cat than the dog. This may be, to some extent, because cats are more cautious and careful animals and it is very unusual for them to step on glass or to tear themselves on barbed wire fences. In any case of severe bleeding as a result of injury to limbs, ears, or tail, apply a firm bandage (see later in this chapter) and contact a Veterinary Surgeon as soon as possible. If blood continues to seep through the dressing it is best to simply apply a little more cotton wool and bandage on top of the first. To remove the dressing may only serve to disturb any clotting which has taken place.

Tourniquet

A tourniquet is a tight ligature that is applied above the site of injury in cases of severe arterial haemorrhage in a limb. However, the risk of gangrene developing if the ligature is left in position for too long is so great that it is much safer for an inexperienced person to apply a large pressure bandage with cotton wool, as described in this chapter.

Internal haemorrhage may often result from road accidents, and is usually serious. It is recognised by extreme pallor of the gums and tongue. Keep the patient warm and contact a Veterinary Surgeon as soon as possible.

It is not wise to attempt to give a cat any liquids by mouth when it is injured. In most cases it will cause struggling which may be harmful and if there are internal injuries, to give anything at all by mouth is dangerous.

APPLYING BANDAGES IN CASES OF FIRST AID

It must be realised that cats are not easy to bandage and the first essential thing to do is to enlist a friend to help in holding the patient. The advice given in the earlier part of the chapter on restraining a cat for examination is even more necessary when dealing with a cat which is hurt in some way.

Before commencing, check that you have everything that you need within easy reach and preferably on a separate table or shelf where it will not be knocked to the floor.

You will probably require any dressings that are to be applied, sterile gauze, cotton wool, bandages, adhesive plaster and scissors.

Fortunately, cats are less inclined to interfere with surgical wounds than dogs and it is not, as a rule, necessary to bandage areas where there are stitches (such as a spay wound), though your Veterinary Surgeon may apply a Elizabethan collar to fretting individuals.

Body

It is rarely possible to bandage a cat's abdomen successfully and it is probably better to construct a cotton jacket to envelop the whole of the cat's body. This need not be very complicated. A simple oblong of material with two holes for the forelegs to go through and a row of fastenings of some kind to secure it in place along the top of the cat's back is usually effective. For a small cat the ribbed area of a man's sock can sometimes be adapted to provide a jacket with more elasticity to keep it in place.

A body bandage suitable for abdominal wounds. If necessary, two holes for the rear legs could be included

andaging foot

If it is necessary to bandage a foot as a result of an accident, it is essential to first clean the wound thoroughly and remove any dirt or grit. Bathe with warm salted water and clip away any hair that is likely to enter the wound and prevent healing. Dust wound with whatever wound dressing has been advised by the Veterinary Surgeon dealing with the case and cover the wound with a piece of sterile gauze.

a. The first stage in bandaging the foot, ensuring that the injured area is well protected.

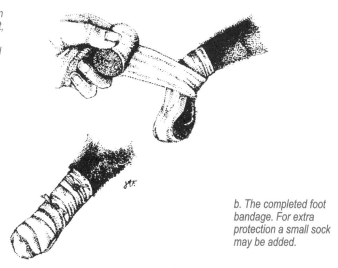

b. The completed foot bandage. For extra protection a small sock may be added.

Next, swathe the limb in a thin layer of cotton wool, tuck a wisp or two of cotton wool under and between the pads to prevent pressure and commence bandaging from the foot up.

Danger of gangrene - It is important to remember that wherever the wound may be on the foot or the limb, it is safer to apply the bandage over a large area and to include the foot. This allows a bandage to be applied firmly but avoids the risk of exerting too much pressure at any point in the leg. If a bandage is applied too tightly half way up a limb there is considerable risk that it will cut off the blood supply and this in turn can cause gangrene, which may be fatal.

Having applied the bandage, finish by criss-cross application of thin adhesive plaster or sticky tape and extend this just beyond the bandage to cover a little of the fur. This will hopefully prevent the dressing from slipping, and it can always be trimmed off carefully with scissors when necessary to avoid discomfort of pulling the hair.

andaging ear

Ears are often damaged when fighting and they can sometimes bleed profusely. If it is not necessary to have the ear stitched the bleeding can be controlled by a firm bandage.

Take a thick pad of cotton wool and place it over the affected ear and wrap a thin layer of cotton wool around the head and neck. Commence bandaging (an elastic bandage is very useful here) in a criss-cross pattern around the head, pressing the injured ear flat against the head but leaving the other ear free to act as a peg to keep the bandage in place. The bandage should extend forward so as just to leave the eyes free and should continue back onto the neck. Great care must be taken to see that the bandage is not applied too tightly under the throat. Finally, again top the bandage with strips of sticky tape to keep it in place.

Ear bandage. The affected ear is covered, while the other is left free to act as an anchor.

Bandaging a tail

This is sometimes necessary and the same general rules apply as for bandaging a limb.It is not usually necessary to include the whole of the tail in the bandage since there is not such a major blood supply at the tip of the tail as in the foot. However, tails are particularly slippery and it may help to fold a few hairs into the bandage as it is applied to help to keep it in place. Take care to apply an even tension when bandaging. Again, it is essential to finish by applying adhesive strips of some kind to cover the bandage and extend into the hair.

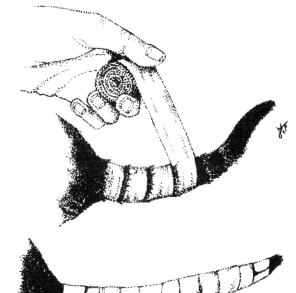

a. When bandaging the tail, include hair in each turn to prevent slippage

b. Finish off with adhesive plaster that extends onto uncovered hair

Abscess formation

It is important to remember that cat wounds very readily become septic, with the formation of abscesses. If you suspect that a wound is infected you should consult a Veterinary Surgeon. Antibiotic treatment, if it is necessary, can do a great deal to reduce the suffering resulting from this type of injury (see also Chapter 7).

Applying skin dressings

Applying skin dressings is never very satisfactory since cats have a strong instinct to lick themselves, and a dressing that was intended to be external can very easily become internal instead.

It will help if a skin dressing or other treatment is applied immediately before feeding the cat so that it has something to distract it. However, if the substance applied is in any way likely to be detrimental if taken by mouth, it is better to use an Elizabethan Collar.

Elizabethan collar

The Elizabethan collar (so called because it resembles the type of ruff worn in the time of Queen Elizabeth) is a very effective method of preventing a cat from biting at stitches, or from making a skin condition worse by constant licking.

A simple Elizabethan Collar made from card and string

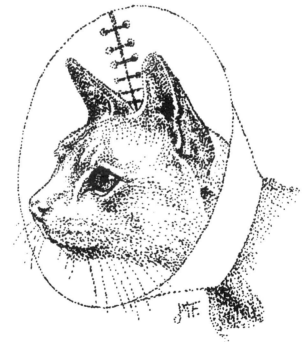

It consists of a piece of thin cardboard or really stiff paper, or plastic, shaped into a funnel, rather like an ice cream cone which the sharp end trimmed off. This is attached to the cat's collar with the funnel projecting forward over the head and face. Some Veterinary Surgeons now supply plastic collars ready made but they can be made quite easily at home.

Injections

It is quite unusual for an owner to be asked to give an injection to a cat and if it should be necessary it will be under the direct guidance of a Veterinary Surgeon in most instances.

However, in case such an emergency should occur (as for instance when living in an isolated place at home or abroad, where Veterinary help may be some distance away) it may be helpful to have some idea of the method to be employed. It will also help the owner who is unused to medical procedures to understand what is involved when the Veterinary Surgeon may have to inject a cat.

The main methods or routes of giving an injection are as follows: -

Intravenous - In this case the injection is given directly into the blood stream, usually through a vein in the foreleg. This is often the method employed when administering anaesthesia.

Intra-peritoneal - The injection is given directly into the abdominal cavity.

Intra-muscular - The injection is given into a muscle - usually the thick muscle of the hind leg or in the back muscles. This route is necessary for some drugs but it is likely to cause a certain amount of pain however carefully given, as a result of the temporary pressure caused by the introduction of the liquid into the dense muscle tissue.

Subcutaneous - This is the most common route for injections and the only one in which an owner is likely to be involved. The injection is given into the space between the skin and the muscle, and causes very little discomfort or distress as a rule. It is usually given into the skin of the scruff of the neck.

Hypodermic syringes

In most cases today syringes are made of plastic and arrive in a sterile plastic pack with a needle already attached, which greatly simplifies the procedure of injections.

First, carefully check the amount of the dose that has to be given. Unwrap the syringe from the plastic cover and read off measurements on the barrel. They will be in cubic centimetres or millilitres (syringes are usually of 1, 2, or 5 cc or ml volume).

Secondly, cleanse the rubber cap of the bottle containing the injection with a little surgical spirit.

Withdraw the plunger of the syringe to the amount of the correct dose, and plunge the needle through the centre of the rubber cap.

Filling the syringe

Invert the bottle and inject air into the bottle (to break vacuum), then withdraw the plunger until the syringe contains fluid up to the appropriate mark and quickly withdraw the needle from the bottle.

Giving the injection

Get an assistant to hold the patient or, if alone, wrap the cat up completely in a blanket, leaving out only the head and sufficient neck to inject. Part hair, and dab the area to be injected with a little surgical spirit. Holding the skin up slightly, plunge the needle through the skin, gently pull the plunger back to ensure that a blood vessel has not accidentally been penetrated, press plunger to expel injection and quickly withdraw the needle. Wipe over the site with cotton wool to disperse the fluid under the skin and to prevent any bleeding.

All this may sound very complicated and intimidating to anyone contemplating giving an injection for the first time. However, practice makes things much easier and an experienced person can give an injection so quickly and painlessly that the patient does not even bother to look round.

Enemas

An enema is a fluid preparation (usually soap and water solution) which is given by injection in the rectum, using a rubber syringe. It is used as a treatment in severe cases of constipation but it is not advisable to attempt it, except under instructions from a Veterinary Surgeon.

CARING FOR THE SICK CAT

There are some conditions, in particular Cat Influenza, in which TLC as it is called today (tender, loving care) can do almost as much as modern drugs in restoring a cat to health.

Cats, when they are well, keep themselves scrupulously clean by licking and grooming. In a condition such as flu, where there is severe nasal and ocular discharge or if there are mouth ulcers, the cat soon becomes soiled, smelly and very wretched. A capable and devoted nurse can work wonders in restoring a cat's psychological well being and through this, his physical welfare as well.

It is true that when a cat is very ill it should not be disturbed too much but equally it should not be neglected. The first sign of returning health in a cat is often when it starts to, half-heartedly at first, wash its face and whiskers.

Keeping clean The eyes and nose should be swabbed several times daily with cotton wool dipped in cool boiled water to remove any discharge. This is especially necessary for the nose, to allow comfortable breathing. A cat that is forced to breathe through its mouth not only suffers distress but also further drying and soreness within the mouth as a result. The whole area of the head should then be dried with a soft flannel or dry cotton wool. The forelegs may be soiled by the cat's attempts to rub its eye and nose. Vaseline should be applied around the nose to prevent further drying and a suitable eye ointment used on the eyes.

If there has been diarrhoea, the tail region can be cleaned in the same way and a dusting of talcum powder can also be applied to help keep the cat fresh and dry.

Force-feeding If it is necessary to force-feed the cat it is important to repeat the cleaning-up process after each meal to prevent stale food accumulating on the hair.

Your cat will not feel like a thorough grooming but a light combing each day will help to remove dead hair and also stimulate the circulation.

Warmth Warmth is essential in this type of illness and unless the eyes are particularly sore, the cat will probably enjoy having his basket moved into the sunshine. Blankets and cushions are inclined to become soiled from discharges and should be changed daily.

Feeding sick cat Cats really hate to be force-fed, so try all possible means to tempt the appetite first. Well-stewed rabbit, hare, or chicken liver are usually popular if they are available, or strong smelling fish, such as kippers or sardines may be useful in cases where the cat has lost his sense of taste and smell.

Offer only small amounts of food at a time and if they are refused take them away. Stale dried-up food is unlikely to tempt a sick animal.

Dehydration (loss of body fluids) is a very serious problem, so make sure your cat's favourite drinks are always available.

It will be noticed that cats in the earlier stages of flu not only sneeze but sometimes literally stream at the mouth, so it is essential to see that not only milk but water is available for the sick cat at all times.

Hunger strike After severe illness some cats appear to lose all interest in food and literally go on a hunger strike. In this case, if the Veterinary Surgeon attending the case agrees, it will probably be necessary to administer liquid foods with a spoon, an eyedropper, or a syringe.

For the very weak cat a mixture of egg white beaten and mixed with one teaspoon of glucose and one teacup of water or Lactol is recommended.

The most satisfactory method of administration is as described earlier in the chapter for giving liquid medicines. The amounts will vary with the cat's willingness to accept the food and swallow but it is better to be content to give only a few teaspoonfuls at a time.

When the cat is feeling stronger and is taking food more readily then sieved meat or fish, or canned baby foods, can sometimes be given quite easily with a spoon.

DISEASES & AILMENTS OF CATS

ABSCESSES

As we have said earlier (Chapter 6) cats are extremely susceptible to abscesses if they receive even the smallest wound, and in particular as a result of bites and scratches from fellow felines or from rats.

Symptoms of swelling and acute pain may be noticed anywhere on the body and the cat will probably be off his food and listless. In the case of a bite to the foot, there may be considerable swelling giving a "frying pan foot" appearance. If the abscess has burst there will be a thick yellow/green, foul-smelling and sometimes bloodstained, discharge and the first indication may be when the cat is seen to be washing itself very vigorously.

Preventative Measures - If you know that your cat has been involved in a fight examine him very carefully all over. If any bites or wounds are found, clip the hair away from the area and bathe with salt water.

Treatment - Once an abscess has developed it is best to consult a Veterinary Surgeon if possible. Treatment with antibiotics can produce an almost instant improvement in the health and well being of the patient and will greatly speed the healing of the wound. If the abscess has developed but has not burst, it may be necessary for the cat to be admitted to a veterinary hospital to have the abscess lanced and drained under anaesthetic.

First Aid Treatment - If no veterinary help is available at the time, the most useful treatment is to clip away all hair from the area of the abscess and to bathe with a luke warm salt solution, several times daily.

Warning   Do not be tempted to allow the abscess to heal too quickly. If the area is not thoroughly bathed to keep the wound open until it has completely drained, a new abscess will quickly form on the same site.

Tooth Abscess - See also Teeth
These occur most often in middle aged or elderly cats. The symptoms are usually refusal to eat, pain when eating, swelling on the side of the cheek, or an unpleasant smell or discharge from the mouth.

Treatment - Consult a Veterinary Surgeon as soon as possible. Even elderly cats will, as a rule, survive the short anaesthetic that is needed for an extraction very well (unless there is any serious heart condition) and the improvement in health will be considerable and well worth the risk. There is no need to feel concerned even if an old cat has to lose all its teeth. Most cats will eat soft prepared cat foods and your pet is unlikely to have any difficulty in eating.

ANAEMIA

This is a symptom rather than a disease. It is characterised by a marked paling of the gums and tongue. It may result from disease but it is also seen when there is internal haemorrhage as a result of road accidents.

Treatment - Consult a Veterinary Surgeon as soon as possible and in the meantime keep the patient quiet and warm.

FELINE INFECTIOUS ANAEMIA

Caused by a microscopic parasite in the blood stream, which can be passed from mother to kitten before birth. It is also spread by bloodsucking parasites (e.g. fleas). Symptoms are variable and not easy for one to identify, so consult your Veterinary Surgeon.

ANAL GLANDS

These are tiny scent glands that are situated at either side of the anus. If the cat becomes frightened it will often release a discharge from the glands, giving a very penetrating and unpleasant smell. Anal glands in dogs are the source of many troubles and disorders but fortunately in cats it is very unusual for them to need any attention at all.

ANAL PROLAPSE- See Prolapse

ARTHRITIS & RHEUMATISM

Elderly cats may suffer from a generalised stiffness and difficulty in walking or jumping. Since it is not at all easy for an owner to diagnose the precise cause it is best to consult a Veterinary Surgeon.

It will help to see that your cat sleeps in a warm dry spot.

Warning - Do not give aspirin. Although it is very helpful to humans with similar conditions, it is poisonous to cats.

ASCITES OR DROPSY

This is a condition in which fluid collects in the abdominal cavity, giving the cat a swollen potbellied look, although it is usually associated with cats that are underweight and in poor condition. It is most often seen in cats as a result of the viral disease Feline Infectious Peritonitis (see later) or some serious internal condition such as a tumour. In either case consult your Veterinary Surgeon as soon as possible.

BAD BREATH

This usually results from bad teeth in middle aged or elderly cats (see abscesses and teeth) but it may also be noticed in young kittens that are changing their milk teeth. Other causes may be mouth ulcers, chronic catarrh, or a tumour in the mouth, or it may result from the presence of a piece of decaying bone which has become lodged in the teeth or from some generalised disorder such as uraemia (kidney failure). In any case, it is a symptom which should not be ignored and which generally responds to treatment, so consult a Veterinary Surgeon as soon as possible.

BALDNESS - ALOPECIA

It is fairly unusual for cats to suffer from a genuine baldness. If your cat develops bare places in the coat it is more often the result of skin parasites (see Chapter 5), or an eczema or dermatitis (see later in this chapter). However, hormonal alopecia is occasionally seen and this can sometimes be treated by administration of hormonal substances by your Veterinary Surgeon.

BITES - See Abscesses

BLADDER TROUBLES

These can be divided into two main problem areas - cystitis (or inflammation of the bladder) and urethral obstruction as a result of calculi, or stones that form in the bladder. These are actually mineral deposits that settle to form tiny stones, or gravel, as they are sometimes called.

Cystitis
This occurs more in female cats than in males. It is characterised by symptoms of pain and the cat will be seen to go to its litter tray frequently and pass small amounts of bloodstained urine. The cat may sit and strain for long periods. There may also be a rise in temperature and signs of generalised illness. Consult a Veterinary Surgeon.

Urethral Obstruction
Now commonly called FUS (Feline Urological Syndrome). This is a very serious condition requiring immediate Veterinary assistance. It is almost unknown in the female cat but occurs in male and neutered cats as a consequence of the formation of bladder stones. The urethra of the male (the passageway connecting the bladder to the penis) is extremely narrow and if tiny particles of gravel are passed in the urine they very readily cause total obstruction. In the female cat, stones of a similar size can be passed with the urine.

Symptoms - The cat will go to its tray and will strain hard but it will be seen that little or no urine is passed. Consult a Veterinary Surgeon as soon as possible. If treatment is not given at once the cat may get blood poisoning or may actually burst its bladder and die. In the meantime it is in great pain.

Treatment - The Veterinary Surgeon may be able to relieve the condition by passing a catheter tube under anaesthesia, but in some cases, penile surgery may be needed if the cat's life is to be saved. Unfortunately this condition has a tendency to recur.

A supply of fresh drinking water should always be provided as part of a cat's normal diet, but if you notice that your cat takes very little water or milk in the course of the day, it is probably better to give dry biscuit as only a small part of the diet, or to use it after first moistening with warm water. Specialist diets are now available to help prevent this condition recurring.

BLEEDING - Haemorrhage - See chapter 6

BRONCHITIS

This occurs most often as a complication of cat flu. It is an inflammation of the bronchi and the bronchioles (the tubes connecting the lung tissue).

Symptoms - Coughing, distressed breathing.

Treatment - Consult a Veterinary Surgeon.

BRUISES

A bruise is actually made up of a mass of pinpoint haemorrhages under the surface of the skin. They do occur in animals but are often missed because of the hair (see Haematomas).

BURNS & SCALDS

These can be a very serious problem in cats and in the case of scalds the full extent of the injuries may not be realised until several days after the event when a large suppurating area is discovered which had been hidden by hair. Severe burns and scalds actually destroy the skin and underlying tissues and the resulting wound may take months to heal completely.

First Aid - In the case of scalds apply cold water over the affected area at once. The cat's coat will otherwise hold the hot liquid and greatly increase the extent of the injuries. Keep the patient warm (since there will be considerable shock) and consult a Veterinary Surgeon as soon as possible. Remember that cats when they are frightened or in pain, have a tendency to bolt, so shut all doors and windows until you are able to get help.

Prevention - Remember that cats are naturally inquisitive so try to avoid leaving them in a room where there is a saucepan of hot liquid, or any similar hazard. They should, of course, be trained for their sake and yours, not to jump onto tables and work surfaces. Many cats suffer from burnt pads as a result of jumping unsuspectingly onto electric hot plates.

CAESAREAN OPERATION - See chapter 2

This operation is carried out to remove kittens by the abdominal route in cases of difficult birth. It is, as a rule, a highly satisfactory method of saving the life of both the mother and kittens but if it becomes necessary it is important for success that it should be carried out as soon as possible. In most cases the mother will be able to feed her kittens and they should be returned to her as soon as she starts to recover from the anaesthetic.

CANCER - See Tumours

CASTRATIONS

This is the name for the neutering operation in the male. See Chapter 2.

CATARACT - See Eye Conditions

CATARRH

This is most often seen as a complication or as a result of Feline Respiratory Disease (cat flu), although there may be other causes.

Symptoms - Sneezing, nasal discharge, sometimes bloodstained. The cat may tend to breathe through his mouth as a result of nasal obstruction. There may be difficulty in smelling and tasting, with a consequent loss of appetite and depression.

Treatment - Antibiotic treatment may give some relief but unfortunately once established this condition is extremely difficult to treat satisfactorily. Consult a Veterinary Surgeon.

See Chapter 6 for advice on practical measures for treatment.

CHLAMYDIA

Chlamydia is an intra-cellular parasite, spread by close contact between cats, or inanimate objects used by infected cats (eg. bowls, toys etc).

Symptoms - chronic conjunctivitis, and can contribute to upper respiratory disease symptoms. A vaccine against chlamydia is now available.

CHOKING

This is fortunately less common in cats than in dogs, since cats are more careful feeders. The most common cause is a large fish bone which has become wedged in the mouth or throat.

Symptoms - Coughing, retching, attempting to vomit, pawing at face.

Diagnosis - To check whether your cat has an obstruction in the throat first examine the mouth and throat as thoroughly as possible in a good light (see Chapter 6 for a safe method of examination). If there is a visible fish bone or other obstruction it may be possible to remove it with tweezers or forceps, but take great care not to get bitten yourself.

Not all foreign bodies or obstructions are visible. If you are in any doubt consult your Veterinary Surgeon immediately. Anaesthesia may be required for a full inspection and removal of any obstruction.

The symptoms of convulsive coughing in the early stages of cat flu can easily be misinterpreted as choking.

CLAWS

These are often broken as a result of fighting. Normally they will grow again, but if the sensitive nail core is exposed the condition is very painful and may require surgery.

Infection of the nail base
In this instance there will be redness and swelling around the base of the nail and the cat will lick the foot constantly and show signs of lameness or pain.

First Aid - Bathe with a warm salt solution but consult a Veterinary Surgeon as soon as possible since antibiotic treatment will probably be needed, or in some cases it may be necessary to remove the nail surgically.

CLEFT PALATE

Congenital
This is a fairly common birth abnormality. It will be noticed that the kitten has difficulty in feeding from the mother, or that milk is tending to come down its nose. On examination it will be seen that the hard palate has failed to fuse completely in the centre. This kitten will rapidly lose condition and will die. Euthanasia is recommended unless a very small defect is found which can be surgically repaired.

Accidental
This may be the result of a car accident, or from a cat falling from a height.

Consult a Veterinary Surgeon as soon as possible. It is a difficult injury but will sometimes respond to surgery.

COCCIDIOSIS

This is a disease characterised by diarrhoea (sometimes bloodstained), accompanied by loss of weight and general condition and sometimes anaemia. It is due to the presence of a protozoan (a minute parasite) in the bowel. It is relatively uncommon in cats in this country. If infection is suspected, consult a Veterinary Surgeon.

CONJUNCTIVITIS - See Eye Conditions

CONSTIPATION

Constipation is not often a problem in cats. If your cat appears to be constipated and is seen to be straining, check thoroughly before attempting treatment. Similar symptoms are shown by cats suffering from acute diarrhoea (when they may strain but only pass a few drops of fluid or blood) or those suffering from urethral obstruction or cystitis (see Bladder Troubles).

Older cats sometimes suffer from a chronic form of constipation which is probably the result of loss of muscle tone in the bowel.

Treatment - Administer Sherley's Cat-a-Med Hairball Remover or a similar preparation daily. If the condition does not improve, consult a Veterinary Surgeon.

The addition of fresh liver to the diet once or twice weekly will often help to counteract a tendency for constipation.

CRYPTORCHIDISM

This is a condition in which the testicles remain in the abdominal cavity instead of descending into the scrotum (in monorchidism only one testicle is affected). See Chapter 3.

DEAFNESS

Congenital Deafness
This occurs in some white cats (usually those with two blue eyes). It cannot be treated and it is a considerable disadvantage since a deaf cat is very vulnerable to its enemies and is in great danger when crossing roads.

Old Age Deafness
Acquired deafness occurs in old cats, especially those with a history of middle or inner ear infections.

Deafness due to impacted wax
This is, in most cases, due to infection with ear mites (see Chapter 5). If in doubt as to the cause of the condition of the ear it is best to consult a Veterinary Surgeon.

DERMATITIS - See Eczema & Dermatitis

DIABETES MELLITUS

This is a condition which results from the failure of the pancreas to produce insulin. It is most often seen in elderly cats.

Symptoms - Loss of weight, together with a pronounced thirst, a good appetite, and excessive urination.

Treatment - Can be given satisfactorily by insulin injections, but much depends on the capacity of the individual owner to carry out the treatment which must be continued throughout the cat's life. Contact a Veterinary Surgeon if you suspect that your cat may be developing this condition.

DIARRHOEA

Diarrhoea is a condition in which the patient passes frequent, loose, or liquid faeces. It may result from many different causes, such as diet (excessive amounts of liver in the food, for instance), viral or bacterial infection, protozoa (coccidia), or bowel parasites.

Treatment of the adult cat - Providing the cat appears well, withhold all food and give only water to drink for 24 hours. If this does not produce an improvement consult a Veterinary Surgeon.

Treatment of kittens - In kittens, diarrhoea should be taken more seriously. It may have resulted from faulty feeding or a roundworm infestation. However, it could be the first symptoms of Feline Virus Enteritis and in any case it may quickly cause symptoms of dehydration in the young animal. Consult a Veterinary Surgeon immediately.

DISLOCATION

A dislocation is the displacement of the articulation point of two bones within the joint capsule. This is comparitively uncommon in the cat.

Hip Dislocation
This is occasionally seen as a result of an accident, resulting in the shortening of the affected leg.

Dislocation of the Jaw
This results in a displacement of the two jaws so that the large canine 'fang' teeth are out of alignment, and the cat is unable to close its mouth. Do not attempt to correct this condition without consulting a Veterinary Surgeon since it may easily be confused with a broken jaw.

As a rule these conditions can be corrected by manipulation under a general anaesthetic providing that they have not been left too long.

DISTEMPER - See Cat Influenza

DROPSY - See Ascites

EAR MITES - See chapter 5

EAR TROUBLES - See Otitis & Haematoma

ECLAMPSIA - Milk Fever

This is a condition of the mother cat while feeding her young, which results from an imbalance of calcium in the blood stream. It is much less common in cats than in dogs.

Symptoms - Muscular twitching or lack of co-ordination, which may be followed by collapse and death if not treated at once. Consult a Veterinary Surgeon immediately.

ECZEMA & DERMATITIS - See also Alopecia

These are the names which are usually applied to inflammations of the skin which are non-parasitic in origin. They are often considered to be allergic in nature; a reaction of the body to a substance. This may be in the food or inhaled but in some cases there may be an allergic reactic to the bite of the flea. Even the presence of one flea on the animal may cause violent itching (see also Chapter 5 - External Parasites).

Symptoms - Irritation and scratching, with hair loss. The affected cat may continuously wash an lick itself, causing serious abrasions with its rough tongue. In other words, the main lesions are self-inflicted.

Miliary Eczema - See Chapter 5

First Aid

a) Make sure that your cat's coat is kept clean and free from tangles and matts which cause irritation.

b) Be certain that your cat is free from parasites. Many owners find it hard to accept that fleas can be found on cats in even the cleanest homes. A Sherley's flea collar, if used according to the instructions, and replaced when necessary, is a most effective method of parasite control.

c) Diet - check that you have not introduced any new foods into the diet which may have caused the symptoms. Try eliminating one item of food (including milk) completely from the diet for a period of two weeks at a time to see if this produces any improvement.

Local Treatment - Calamine Lotion applied with a pad of cotton wool will give some local relief. However, it is important to remember that any external treatment which is given to a cat is liable to become internal as a result of licking. It may help if the cat wears an Elizabethan Collar for several hours after the dressing or lotion is applied (see Chapter 6).

If these simple measures produce no improvement do consult a Veterinary Surgeon. Modern anti-inflammatory drugs can do much to alleviate the distressing symptoms of eczema and dermatitis, but it is as well to recognise that the condition is very likely to recur.

ENTERITIS - Non Specific Enteritis - See Diarrhoea

FELINE IMMUNODEFICIENCY VIRUS (FIV)

This unpleasant virus is related to the Human Immunodeficiency Virus (HIV). However, it is not infectious to people.

Symptoms - chronic oral, respiratory and adenoidal infections, and associated diarrhoea. Transmitted from cat to cat, usually via saliva. Diagnosed using a blood test.

There is no treatment, and infected cats can only be made to feel more comfortable with medication.

FELINE VIRAL ENTERITIS

This is a serious and often fatal viral disease which mainly affects young cats. Its incidence is greatest in pet shops, catteries, and lost cats' homes because of the increased risk of contact with infected cats. However, it may occur in private homes also.

Incubation Period - Symptoms are thought to develop at four to ten days after contact with an infected cat. It is for this reason that a kitten which seemed perfectly well when it arrived in a new home can after a week become acutely ill and die.

Symptoms - Infected cats are very ill, and time is of the essence. Vomiting is usually the first symptom, followed by a loss of appetite and diarrhoea. There may be a rise in temperature. The cat is thirsty and may often be found in the sink or in a drain. There is abdominal pain and typically the patient sits in a hunched-up position and even cries out. Young kittens very quickly become dehydrated and emaciated and for kittens of under twelve weeks the death rate is very high.

Treatment - Consult a Veterinary Surgeon immediately. Antibiotics, intravenous fluids and other drugs will help to give some relief from the symptoms. See also Chapter 6 for advice on general care of the sick cat.

Prevention - Vaccination may be carried out against Feline Enteritis and is highly effective (see Chapter 3). However, it must be realised that prevention will not be effective if the cat is in the early stages of the disease.

Booster injections are needed to maintain a level of immunity (consult your own Veterinary Surgeon about this) and this is particularly important if your cat has to go into boarding kennels.

EUTHANASIA

If your cat has become too old to take any pleasure in life, or if it is suffering from some painful condition from which there is no prospect of permanent relief it is much kinder to ask your Veterinary Surgeon to put your pet painlessly to sleep. This should also be considered if, for personal reasons you find that you are no longer able to keep your cat. By all means try and find new, good home for him, but it need hardly be said that genuine cat lovers will never pass a pet on to just any home and will certainly not consider abandoning an animal because they are unable to face a difficult decision.

Euthanasia is now almost always performed by means of injection of an overdose of an anaesthetic drug, which puts the animal into a stage of deep sleep which is followed by narcosis and death. The injection itself is not, as a rule, painful, but if you dread the thought or if your cat i very nervous ask your Veterinary Surgeon for a sedative tablet which can be given in advance.

The decision to have a loved pet put to sleep is always a very hard one to make but the deciding factor must always be to put the comfort and welfare of the animal concerned first, rather than an consideration for your own emotions.

EYE CONDITIONS

Cataract
This is an opacity of the lens of the eye, which gives it a cloudy appearance and results in partia or complete loss of vision. It is seen most in elderly cats but is not a common condition. Surgery possible, but is not usually recommended.

Conjunctivitis
This is an inflammation of the membrane of the eye.

Symptoms - Irritation, redness or soreness of the eye, or sometimes a discharge from the eyes

It may occur as an isolated condition or may be a complication of cat flu.

First Aid Measures - Bathe the eyes in cool water which has been previously boiled, but consu a Veterinary Surgeon for advice on further treatment.

Glaucoma
This is a condition in which there is an increased pressure within the eye, giving a rather swollen "glassy" look. Most common in elderly cats, and as a complication of cataract. This can be very painful and requires prompt veterinary treatment.

Haw (or Third Eyelid)
Cats have a third eyelid or protective membrane in the corner of the eye. When there is any condition causing irritation of one or both eyes, the third lid will tend to come over the eyeball an

this is quite normal (although owners seeing the condition for the first time sometimes assume that the cat is going blind).

Sometimes the condition of the third eyelid, or "haws" as it is sometimes called, occurs when there is no obvious local reason and it is thought that it may be a symptom of generalised loss of condition. If it persists consult a Veterinary Surgeon.

Kittens' Eyes
Remember that kittens do not normally open their eyes until the tenth to fourteenth day of life.

Prolapse of the Eyeball
This can occur as a result of fighting or road accidents. It may be possible for the eye to be returned to its socket successfully under anaesthesia but if the eye is damaged it is better to have it removed. A cat will manage very well with only one eye.

Staining
This condition around the eyes may result from a blocked tear duct causing an overflow of tears. Consult a Veterinary Surgeon.

Ulcers
Eye ulcers are less common in cats than in dogs. They are seen as pinpoint bluish opaque areas on the eye and cause considerable discomfort. Consult a Veterinary Surgeon.

FELINE INFECTIOUS PERITONITIS

This disease causes fluid to collect in the abdomen leading to "dropsy" or acites. Fluid may also collect in the chest causing breathing difficulties.

It is caused by a virus but the disease is often complicated in cats that are also infected with Feline Leukaemia Virus. There is no cure but your Veterinary Surgeon may be able to relieve some of the symptoms.

FELINE RESPIRATORY VIRUS - See Influenza

FISH HOOKS

Cats sometimes become involved with fish hooks because of their liking for fish. It is important to remember that most hooks have barbs on the end and cannot be pulled out. In most cases it is necessary to consult a Veterinary Surgeon who will be able to remove the fish hook quite easily and painlessly under an anaesthetic.

FITS OR CONVULSIONS

These are fortunately fairly uncommon in cats but they may be rather alarming at the time. The cat may stagger, and then rush about the room, apparently unable to see and banging into furniture and walls.

High blood pressure and thiamine (Vitamin B1) deficiency have been found to be a cause of fits.

First Aid - Do not attempt to touch the cat, but shut doors and windows and try to prevent it from harming itself too much. Consult a Veterinary Surgeon as soon as possible.

FLEAS - One of the most common cat problems - See Chapter 5

FRACTURES

Fractures are only too common as a result of road accidents. Treatment will depend on the site but an owner should never attempt to splint a leg as it could well cause more damage. Keep the patient quiet and immobilised in a basket or box and consult a Veterinary Surgeon as soon as possible.

Fractures of limbs are commonly repaired by means of an internal pin or a metal plate.

Green Stick Fracture
These fractures may occur in young cats. The fracture line is incomplete.

Compound Fractures
These involve an open wound at the site.

Hard Palate Fractures - See Cleft Palate.

Pelvic Fractures
These are very common. Treatment is mainly by immobilisation and recovery is dependent largel on the age of the patient and the number of pelvic bones that have been affected. Healing may cause a narrowing of the pelvic canal, so it is best that female cats should be spayed as soon as possible after recovery to avoid the risk of birth complications.

Jaw Fractures
The most common site (especially in young cats) is the centre of the lower jaw. Treatment by wiring the jaw is usually very successful but it can be necessary to hand-feed the patient for the first seven to ten days (see Chapter 6).

FELINE UROLOGICAL SYNDROME (FUS) - See Bladder Tr

HAIRBALLS

During the moulting season, cats (especially longhaired cats) swallow enormous amounts of hai and this can form a hard ball in the stomach. In most cases these hairballs are vomited quite harmlessly. Obviously if you groom your cat regularly the chances of a hairball developing will be much less.

Cats are also inclined to chew string - especially if it has been around meat, and this can cau a similar obstruction in the stomach.

Treatment - Administer Sherley's Cat-a-Med Hairball Remover on a regular basis, but if your ca is vomiting or seems unwell consult a Veterinary Surgeon.

HAEMATOMA

This is a haemorrhage under the skin and may occur anywhere on the body as a result of a blow. It is usually seen as a darkish, not very painful swelling. It may easily be confused with an abscess which is much more of a common type of injury in the cat. However, in a case of an haematoma, there is far less pain on examination.

HAEMATOMA IN THE EAR

This is a common condition in the cat. It may result from a fight, or an accident, or as a result of shaking the head because of irritation caused by ear mites (see Chapter 5).

Appearance - There will be a swelling on the flap of the ear, varying from the size of a small marble to one which totally fills the ear flap.

Treatment - Consult a Veterinary Surgeon as an operation will be necessary to relieve the pressure and to try to keep the shape of the ear intact. If left, the ear will, as a rule, crumple and scar giving the typical appearance of the "battered" tom.

Don't forget to check for ear mites and treat for these as well.

HAEMATURIA

Blood in the urine may be seen as a result of an accident causing internal bleeding or as a result of infection (see Bladder Troubles).

HAEMORRHAGE - See Bleeding

HEART DISEASE

This is fortunately quite uncommon in cats. Some middle-aged and elderly cats may develop heart murmurs and show symptoms of lassitude and shortness of breath. Consult a Veterinary Surgeon if you suspect this condition.

HEAT - Oestrus or Calling - See chapter 2

HERNIA

A hernia or rupture is the prolapse of viscera (usually abdominal contents or fat) through a gap in the muscle wall.

Umbilical & Inguinal Hernia
Rarely seen but both require surgical correction when they occur.

Diaphragmatic Rupture
This may occur as a result of an accident. The stomach, intestines, or other viscera are herniated into the chest due to a tear in the diaphragm. The cat will show distressed breathing and will be afraid to lie down. The condition is very serious so consult a Veterinary Surgeon.

INCONTINENCE

Lack of control over bladder and bowels can be seen in older cats. It very much depends upon the individual case but the prospect is, as a rule, poor. Consult a Veterinary Surgeon.

Incontinence or dribbling of urine in a young male cat may indicate the first signs of urethral obstruction (see Bladder Troubles and Spraying).

INFLUENZA - CAT FLU - FELINE RESPIRATORY VIRUS INFEC

Cat flu, as it is commonly called, is a disease which occurs mainly in situations where many cats share a close area. Some cats may be carriers of the disease which they transmit to other cats without themselves showing symptoms.

The main types of the disease have been identified as: -

a) Feline Calici Virus (FCV)
This is a milder form of the disease and is characterised by sneezing, discharging eyes, and sometimes ulceration of the mouth.

b) Feline Viral Rhinotracheitis
A very severe and sometimes fatal type of the disease. Early symptoms are similar - typically sneezing, excessive salivation, loss of appetite, and sometimes a high temperature. Later the nasal discharge becomes purulent, pneumonia may develop and the cat soon becomes dehydrated and depressed.

Cases of either type which recover can be left with permanent catarrhal discharge from the eyes and nose.

Treatment - Consult a Veterinary Surgeon at once, but this is a situation in which good home nursing and care can also do much to help (see Chapter 6).

Prevention - A number of vaccines are available now against this disease. Consult your own Veterinary Surgeon about the most suitable vaccine for your own cat, and be sure to take your cat back for regular booster doses when necessary.

Disinfection - Cat flu is spread by droplet infection, and the risk of spread is very great. In the case of the private home it is kinder to warn other cat owners to stay away until the infection is completely cleared. In catteries disinfection is extremely difficult. Cages should be scrubbed out with a solution of disinfectant in hot water and the building should be fumigated.

JAUNDICE

This is a symptom rather than a disease. Typically the tongue, gums, and whites of the eyes and skin develop a yellowish tinge and the urine is dark yellow or brownish. It may be an indication of infection, poisoning, or even a tumour of the liver. Consult a Veterinary Surgeon at once.

KIDNEY DISEASE - NEPHRITIS

This is a fairly common disease of middle-aged to elderly cats. The symptoms are due probably a mild and often unnoticed kidney infection early in life causing damage to the kidney structure which becomes progressively more serious. The kidneys are unable to perform their normal function of filtering impurities and waste products out of the blood.

Symptoms - Thirst, loss of appetite, loss of weight and increased urination. Occasional vomiting and in the later stages an unpleasant uraemic, or ammoniacal smell to the breath.

Treatment - Consult a Veterinary Surgeon. While the condition cannot be cured, treatment may help alleviate the symptoms and prolong life.

LAMENESS

This is an indication of pain in a limb (or sometimes the spine or pelvis). In cats the reason is much more often a septic bite than a strain or sprain.

LEPTOSPIROSIS (Leptospira canicola)

This common cause of kidney disease in dogs is extremely uncommon in cats.

It is caused by Leptospira icterohaemorrhagiae, which is spread by rats and quite commonly affects dogs, but is almost unknown in cats.

LEUKAEMIA (FELINE LEUKAEMIA VIRUS)

This is being recognised today as a widespread viral disease of cats. It is a disorder of the white blood cells. It may lead to a cat being prone to many other diseases, eg. peritonitis, pleurisy or tumours. The disease is passed by very close cat to cat contact.

Symptoms - There may be a wide variety of symptoms such as generalised loss of condition and weight, intermittent rises in temperature, thirst, anaemia, and ulceration of the mouth. All of these symptoms can make the disease rather difficult to identify.

Fortunately, medical research has proven that the disease in cats is not transmissable to humans. The disease can be tested for by your Veterinary Surgeon taking a small blood sample from your cat.

A vaccination to protect against this disease is also available.

LICE - See chapter 5 - External Parasites

MASTITIS

This is an inflammation of the mammary glands, seen usually in the mother cat which is feeding a litter.

Symptoms - Redness and swelling of the mammary glands, raised temperature, pain and disinclination to let the kittens feed.

Treatment - Consult a Veterinary Surgeon. Antibiotic treatment will, as a rule, produce a dramatic improvement.

MANGE

Sarcoptic and Demodectic mange are very rare in the cat (see Chapter 5).
Notoedric (head) mange is sometimes seen (see Chapter 5).

METRITIS (Infection of the womb)

This is an extremely serious and often fatal condition which may follow kittening. It may occur if the cat has failed to deliver all of the kittens or all of the placentas (afterbirths), or simply as a result of infection (see Chapter 2).

Symptoms - A purulent or bloodstained vulval discharge, rise in temperature, lassitude, loss of appetite, and disinclination to care for the kittens.

Consult a Veterinary Surgeon at once.

MILK FEVER - See Eclampsia

This should not be confused with mastitis - the two conditions are not related in any way.

NAILS - See Claws

NYSTAGMUS

This is a condition in which the eyeballs move constantly from side to side. It is seen in cases of concussion and infection of the middle ear.

OTITIS EXTERNA

A general name for conditions affecting the canal of the ear.

Bacterial Infection
Because cats have "pricked" ears they are fairly free from bacterial infections. In the dog (or at least the long-eared varieties) the ear flap tends to create a moist atmosphere within the canal which is ideal for bacterial growth. However, if your cat should show any sign of discharge from the ear consult a Veterinary Surgeon.

Parasitic Otitis
This is extremely widespread among cats as a result of ear mite infections. Cats are very clean animals but the canal of the ear is one spot which they cannot reach. The condition is recognised by the presence of black wax in the ear canal. See Chapter 5 - External Parasites - for details of diagnosis and treatment.

Tumours in the Ear
These are unfortunately rather common, especially in older cats. There is usually a very unpleasant smelling discharge from the ear and the cat will scratch the ear, or keep the head on one side. Consult a Veterinary Surgeon. An operation may give relief, but unfortunately these tumours are occassionally malignant in nature (see Tumours).

PAINT

Cats seem to get themselves involved with wet paint quite often and the results can be very unpleasant (this also applies to tar).

NEVER USE TURPENTINE OR OTHER PAINT SOLVENTS AS THESE ARE EXTREMELY POISONOUS TO CATS. These will not only be licked off, but will also be absorbed through the skin. Cut as much hair and paint off as possible and then rub butter or margarine into the remainder and remove with warm water and liquid detergent. Consult a Veterinary Surgeon.

PARALYSIS

The result of damage to, or degeneration of nerves. The seriousness varies with the site.

Radial Paralysis
This usually follows a blow to the shoulder damaging the radial nerve.

Symptoms - Loss of function and loss of feeling in the fore limb. The cat is unable to pick up the foot, which quickly becomes damaged and excoriated, and will become gangrenous if not treated.

Recovery is poor. If there is no improvement in three to four weeks there is little chance of recovery. Amputation of the limb may be considered if the Veterinary Surgeon advises it. Cats and dogs manage remarkably well on three legs.

Paralysis of the Tail
This is a very common result of injury. Again the symptoms are loss of sensation and loss of movement, and the trailing tail soon becomes damaged.

Amputation holds out a good prospect for success. A tail really is not missed at all (Manx cats manage very well without one).

PARAPLEGIA (Paralysis of hind limbs)

Posterior paralysis usually results from an injury to the spine, often after road accidents. In most cases control of the bladder and bowels are lost as well as the ability to support the body on the hind limbs. If no improvement is seen within seven days, the chances of recovery are very poor indeed.

PLEURISY

This is an extremely serious condition resulting from an inflammation of the folds of tissue which separate the lungs. It may exist as a condition on its own or may follow Feline Respiratory Virus, Feline Leukaemia Virus, or Feline Infectious Peritonitis.

Symptoms - Very high temperature, distressed breathing, inability to lie down. The symptoms may be quite sudden in onset.

In exudative pleurisy there is free pus in the chest cavity and the condition is very rapidly fatal. Pleurisy of any kind can prove difficult to treat.

PNEUMONIA

An inflammation of the lung tissue. There is usually a raised temperature and audible and distressed breathing. It can be a common complication of Feline Respiratory Virus infection. Antibiotics, in many cases, produce a rapid improvement.

POISONING

Fortunately, because cats are rather careful feeders, they suffer less from the results of accidental poisoning than dogs. Puppies will gobble up and swallow almost any strange thing and dogs of any age will eat dead carcasses that they find on walks but this behaviour is almost unknown in cats.

Malicious Poisoning
When people have neighbours who do not like cats there is a tendency to suspect that any illness which their pet may suffer is a result of malicious poisoning. Before jumping to conclusions, it is worth considering the previous paragraph; normally well fed cats are unlikely to eat contaminated food and in addition the majority of people do not have access to dangerous poisons.

Carbolic Acid (Phenol) Poisoning
Since cats are very susceptible to phenol and can absorb it through the skin, any substance suspected of containing it should be avoided. Some disinfectants contain phenols.

Symptoms - Twitching and convulsions followed by collapse and often death.

Turpentine Poisoning
This is very similar to phenol poisoning and will often result from well-intentioned attempts to remove paint (see Paint).

Aspirin
While it is a useful drug for humans (and dogs), it can prove fatal to cats.

Anticoagulants
These are products such as warfarin, used to poison and kill vermin. It is possible for a cat to eat a poisoned rat or mouse.

Symptoms - Acute internal haemorrhaging, manifested by pain, depression and coldness. May be rapidly fatal. Seek veterinary advice immediately.

Ethylene Glycol (anti-freeze)
It is not uncommon for some cats to lick this.

Symptoms - Depression, increased thirst, vomiting and convulsions, renal failure, damaged blood vessels in the brain, lack of coordination, and eventually, coma.

What to do if you know your cat has been poisoned:-

If you are certain that your cat has swallowed a poisonous substance, attempt to make him vomit. The best thing to use is a small (marble size) piece of washing soda, or a strong solution of salt and water (see Chapter 6 - Administration). Contact a Veterinary Surgeon immediately and tell him which poison is concerned. As a general rule, if no help is available remember that acid poisons should be treated by giving an alkaline solution. Bicarbonate of Soda is the most likely one to be available in the home. Alkali poisons may be counteracted by giving vinegar diluted 50% with water.

In the case of external poisons (Lysol etc), if possible, remove the irritant substance by washing in warm soap and water. Keep the patient warm and contact a Veterinary Surgeon immediately.

It need hardly be said that no sensible owner will introduce rat or mouse poisons, or weed killers into the house or garden before checking that they are safe for use with pets.

PROLAPSE

This refers, as a rule, to the extrusion of either the uterus (usually following kittening) or part of the bowel (usually as a result of diarrhoea). This is a serious condition and it is important to consult a Veterinary Surgeon as soon as possible (see Chapter 2).

Young kittens suffering from diarrhoea may suffer a slight prolapse or protrusion of the rectum and treating the cause (see Diarrhoea) will produce some improvement. However, if the condition persists Veterinary help should be sought.

PYOMETRA

This is a condition in which pus forms in the uterus and is comparatively uncommon in the cat. This may be, to some extent, because the majority of female cats are now spayed. When it exists it usually follows a history of irregular oestrus as a result of cystic ovaries.

Symptoms - A vaginal discharge, listlessness, loss of appetite, and thirst. Consult a Veterinary Surgeon as soon as possible. Surgery is almost always necessary.

RABIES

An extremely dangerous and usually fatal disease of man and animals. It does not exist in this country because of our very strict quarantine laws that have been in force over the years, and, more recently, vaccination.

Rabies vaccination - This is not carried out on pets living in this country, but may be necessary if you plan to take your cat abroad. Check with your own Veterinary Surgeon.

RANULA

A soft swelling under the tongue which may be due to a blocked or infected salivary duct. Any unusual swelling in the mouth should always be examined by your Veterinary Surgeon.

RICKETS

A condition of poor bone formation in the young animal resulting from an imbalance of the calcium and phosphorus ratio in the diet. It is important to remember that in the wild state cats would eat the bones of their prey thus ensuring an adequate supply of minerals. A diet which contains the correct proportion of minerals for a normal adult cat may be insufficient for the pregnant cat or kitten.

Symptoms - Lameness, or "knuckling" over at knee joints. Consult a Veterinary Surgeon. It is an extremely rare condition in the UK.

RHEUMATISM - See Arthritis & Rheumatism

ROAD ACCIDENTS - See chapter 6

RODENT ULCER

This actually has no connection with rats or mice at all. It was probably so-called because it occurs on the upper lip of the cat (usually near the median line) and was thought to result from catching rats.

It is a hard, dry, ulcerated area which is very slow to heal. Although initially it causes little distress to the patient, if left untreated, it can spread and cause erosion of the lip.

Treatment - Gentian violet was once used, but today modern drugs are more effective. Consult a Veterinary Surgeon.

RUBBER BAND

Children often slip rubber bands on the legs or around the neck of pets while playing. If they are not removed they may cause serious, deep wounds.

RUPTURE - See Hernia

SALIVATION

Excessive salivation is one of the first signs of Feline Respiratory Virus. It may also indicate a foreign body such as a bone stuck in the mouth, mouth ulcers, gum disease, a bad tooth (see Teeth), a bee sting, or maybe because your cat has licked some irritant substance. Consult a Veterinary Surgeon.

SCABIES - See Mange

SCALDS - See Burns & Scalds

SPAYING

This is the name for neutering in the female. See Chapter 3.

SPRAINS

Fairly uncommon in cats, since they are very skillful at landing on their feet. Occasionally strained back muscles are seen, possibly as a result of a misjudged jump.

SPRAYING

Unneutered male cats are inclined to urinate or "spray" walls and furniture even in their own homes, especially in the breeding season. Rather inexplicably, occasional cases of spraying are seen in neutered males and females.

STINGS

Most cats at some time attempt to catch a wasp or a bee, before learning a very painful lesson. In some cases there may be a considerable allergic reaction and the cat may salivate and be very distressed. If it is possible to contact a Veterinary Surgeon the administration of an anti-histamine drug will usually give immediate relief. However, the symptoms will, as a rule, subside on their own in one or two hours.

TAIL INJURIES

Cats' tails, being rather exposed, are very liable to injury. Treatment depends very much on the cause. See abscesses and paralysis in this chapter, and "how to bandage a tail" in Chapter 6.

TAPEWORM - See chapter 5 - Internal Parasites

TEETH

Cats, just like people, have two sets of teeth; the "baby" or milk teeth and the adult permanent teeth which are cut in the period 12 to 24 weeks of age. Teething does not cause much trouble to young kittens as a rule but very occasionally the milk teeth may fail to shed as the new teeth develop, giving a double set, which sometimes leads to a painful or infected mouth.

The adult cat has a total of thirty teeth:

Upper jaw:	6 tiny incisors at the front
	2 large canines at the corners
	6 premolars
	2 molars
Lower jaw:	6 incisors
	2 canines
	4 premolars
	2 molars

Tartar
Many cats form heavy deposits of "tartar" composed of mineral salts around the teeth, and the deposits can often be considerably larger than the teeth themselves. If this is not removed it causes soreness of the gums, bad breath, salivating, and loss of appetite. It may result in gingivitis and periodontal disease which leads to tooth decay. Cats suffer from true dental caries, many of which can be extremely painful.

Regular scaling by your Veterinary Surgeon (usually under anaesthetic) can do much to prevent tartar and to keep the gums and teeth healthy. However, you can carry out a dental regime for your cat at home, and there are many dental products now available (such as the Sherley's toothbrush and paste set) which, once you get your cat used to the idea, can be relatively easy to carry out.

Broken Teeth
The canine teeth in particular are often broken when fighting. If they are not causing pain they can be left, but infection may lead to the formation of tooth abscesses, in which case consult a Veterinary Surgeon. Extraction may be necessary.

Bad teeth should be removed under general anaesthetic. Once removed, the gums harden and the teeth are hardly missed. See also "Tooth Abscess" under Abscesses.

TEMPERATURE

For "how to take a temperature" see Chapter 6.

THIRD EYELID - See Conditions of the Eye

THIRST - See chapter 6

TRAVEL SICKNESS

This is not common in cats. If a cat is a poor traveller, avoid feeding before a journey and if necessary ask the Veterinary Surgeon for a suitable sedative.

TONGUE

Injuries
The tongue is often injured in the course of fights, or from licking out tin cans, and may bleed profusely. Small tears and cuts will heal on their own but if bleeding persists consult a Veterinary Surgeon.

Ulceration
Small smooth or pinkish areas will be seen on the tongue and there is usually excessive salivatic and loss of appetite. Consult a Veterinary Surgeon (see Ulcerative Glossitis).

TOXOPLASMOSIS

Although cats are often infected with this organism, they only rarely show signs of the disease, characterised by a high temperature and very varied symptoms. Diagnosis is not easy and depends on serological examination. This organism poses a small risk to pregnant women who should avoid handling cat faeces or litter trays.

TUMOURS

A tumour is produced by the abnormal growth of tissue cells. The very mention of the word is alarming to an owner, but it is important to remember that tumours may be benign as well as malignant and this greatly influences the future outlook. Tumours may occur at almost any site, or on, the body (even in bones) and the severity of the problem involved may depend to a large extent on their situation, for example, a tumour on the tongue or in the ear canal quickly become intolerable.

Benign Tumours
The multiplication of cells is confined to a single site and if surgically removed they will not, as a rule, return.

Malignant Tumours (Cancers)
These not only tend to return at the same site, but are also liable to spread throughout the body.

If you suspect that your cat is suffering from a tumour consult a Veterinary Surgeon immediately.

You may be quite mistaken in your diagnosis, or if it is a tumour it may be "benign". To delay asking advice through fear may cause your pet unnecessary suffering and may lessen the chances of successful treatment.

ULCERATIVE GLOSSITIS

This may occur as a separate entity or may be associated with Feline Respiratory Virus or kidney disease. Ulcers appear on the tongue, there is marked salivation, loss of appetite, extreme bad breath, and sometimes a rise in temperature. Consult a Veterinary Surgeon.

VACCINATION

Vaccination against the main viral diseases is an important step in your cat's health programme (see Chapter 3).

VOMITING

Vomiting in dogs and cats is extremely common and is, to some extent, a natural means of protection in ridding the body of noxious substances. However, persistent vomiting is a danger signal, and in these circumstances it is best to consult a Veterinary Surgeon (see also Chapter 6).

WORMS - See chapter 5

WOUNDS - See Abscesses & chapter 6

SHERLEY'S CAT CARE PRODUCTS

SHERLEY'S FLEA PREPARATIONS

Flea Collars for Cats (Felt)

Neat felt collars in a range of different colours containing an insecticide giving up to 4 months protection against fleas. When worn continuously, and used in conjunction with an environmental flea control product, they can prevent further reinfestation. The collars incorporate an elasticated safety buckle, come in three colours, and can be used on cats and kittens over 12 weeks of age.

Flea Collars for Cats (Reflective)

A variation on the above, but with a flourescent finish to help ensure your cat is seen in the dark winter evenings and nights.

Flea Collars for Cats (Plastic)

Neat plastic collars in a range of different colours containing an insecticide giving up to 4 months protection against fleas. When worn continuously, and used in conjunction with an environmental flea control product, they can prevent further reinfestation. The collars incorporate a unique safety release buckle, are waterproof, and can be used on cats over 6 months of age.

Lost & Found Flea Collar for Cats (Plastic)

Not only does this collar give 4 months protection against fleas, it also doubles up as an identification collar. Each collar has its own unique identity number printed on it that you register free of charge direct with Sherley's. Should your cat become lost, the finder can ring the Freephone number which is also printed on the collar, and Sherley's can help reunite you with your pet. These collars are recyclable and are for use on cats over 6 months of age.

Big Red Flea Spray

A highly effective aerosol spray for controlling fleas on cats and kittens over 12 weeks of age. Best results are obtained when used in conjunction with any of the Sherley's environmental flea control products.

Permethrin Flea Powder

Permethrin Powder can be used on cats and kittens over 12 weeks of age. You simply rub it into the coat and then brush out. Best results are obtained when used in conjunction with any of the Sherley's environmental flea control products.

Pump Action Flea Spray

The specially designed low noise pump mechanism enables the treatment of cats and kittens over 12 weeks of age who are worried by the "hissing" noise of aerosol sprays. Pump Action Flea Spray kills fleas, and can be used in conjunction with any of the Sherley's flea control products to help prevent reinfestation.

Defest II

This easily applied aerosol spray gives lasting protection from fleas and other nuisance insects in the home. One application gives up to 12 weeks control in carpets and pet bedding.

Flego

A houshold flea spray for the environmentally-conscious, the spray contains a short-acting insecticide to kill fleas and their larvae on contact, and an insect growth regulator for long-term control. One application lasts for up to one year.

Flea Buster

A non-insecticidal household flea powder which works by dehydration of fleas, their eggs, and their larvae. Simply brush into the carpets and soft furnishings, and vacuum up any residue. One application lasts for up to one year.

Rug-de-Bug

A pleasantly scented insecticidal carpet freshener. Simply sprinkle on and vacuum up to control fleas and odours around the home.

SHERLEY'S TICK PREPARATIONS

Tick Away

An easy-to-use spray for the removal of ticks from your cat. Simply part the fur and spray directly onto the tick, which will die and automatically fall off within 3 hours.

SHERLEY'S WORMING PREPARATIONS

Worming Syrup

A specially formulated, chocolate flavoured syrup for roundworm eradication in kittens from 2 weeks of age. Roundworm infestations are transmitted from mother to kittens, and therefore routine treatment is advisable. Now available in an easy-to-use pump dispenser.

Worming Cream

A specially formulated, palatable cream for roundworm eradication in kittens from 2 weeks of age. It's pleasant flavour means that it can be placed on the nose, around the mouth, or on a biscuit, and will be readily licked off. Now available in an easy-to-use syringe.

Worming Granules for Cats

An easy, no-nonsense solution to routine worming. The granules are virtually tasteless and odour-free and are simply sprinkled onto the food. For use in cats over 6 months of age.

Multiwormer for Cats

A three-week combination course of tablets for the treatment of roundworm and tapeworm in cats over 6 months of age.

SHERLEY'S VITAMINS AND TONICS

Vionate

A balanced vitamin and mineral mix, specially formulated to supplement the diet of your cat. Regularly administered, Vionate can improve general health and appearance, and help assure a long, active, healthy life. The product is particularly beneficial to pregnant and lactating queens, and to cats in their elderly years. Available in 2 pack sizes (120 g and 500 g).

Calcium Tablets

With added Vitamin D to assist intestinal absorption, this important mineral is essential to the formation of strong teeth and bones. Particularly valuable for young, pregnant, or lactating animals.

Cooling Tablets

Cooling Tablets contain a special combination of ingredients to tone and refresh the system. They can be of particular value when taken during the warmer months of the year.

Gastrine Tablets

Help balance digestion in sensitive stomachs.

SHERLEY'S OTHER TREATMENTS & ACCESSOF

Deodorant Tablets

Specially formulated to control breath and body odours in cats.

Breath Freshener Tablets

Specially formulated to help provide long term action for cats with breath odour. Tablets may be taken whole or crumbled and mixed with food.

Cat-a-Med Hairball Remover

Simply spread onto food or give directly to control the problem of hairballs caused by cats' grooming habits.

Ear Cleaner

Specially formulated to aid the removal of wax and other debris from the ear canal.

Eye Lotion

Specially formulated to gently soothe and clean the eyes. This can also be used to wipe clean tear stains.

Spray Away

A harmless spray for regular use around the home to neutralise animal odours on furniture and furnishings and to deodorise baskets and bedding. Pay particular attention to corners and crevices.

Swiftie Trainer

Has a special attractant odour, almost unnoticeable to humans. Used
regularly on a newspaper or tray which is each time moved nearer the door, kittens are quickly
and cleanly house trained.

SHERLEY'S FOODS

Lactol

Lactol is a milk food, scientifically formulated as a replacement or supplement for kittens and is
also highly suitable for pregnant or nursing queens as an addition to the diet. Lactol contains all of
the nutrients of natural queen's milk, plus added vitamins, in an easily digestible form. Available in
four different pack sizes (250 g, 500 g, 1 kg and 1.5 kg).

SHERLEY'S GROOMING AIDS

Grooming Spray

A non-greasy, rapidly drying grooming tonic that beautifies and imparts a rich glossy sheen to the
hair. Used by breeders and exhibitors to add the final touch to the cat's appearance. Available in
an easy-to-use pump-action spray.

Tea Tree Shampoo

A conditioning shampoo, made with Australian tea tree oil, to soothe minor skin problems and help
prevent dandruff.

Diagnos Anti-Dandruff Shampoo

For flaky and itchy skin, with dandruff. Soothes and rehydrates the skin. Contains Methyl
Sulphonyl Methane (MSM), calendula oil and salicylic acid.

Diagnos Anti-Itch Shampoo

For "Itchy" cats. Eases skin inflammation and irritation. Contains Methyl Sulphonyl Methane
(MSM), aloe vera and lemon grass.

Diagnos Hypoallergenic Shampoo

An extremely mild shampoo, developed for highly sensitive skin. Contains Methyl Sulphonyl
Methane (MSM), to aid in the relief of skin allergies.

SHERLEY'S CAT & KITTEN CARE PRODUCTS

Sherley's Flea Preparations

Flea Collar For Cats (Felt)
Flea Collar For Cats (Reflective)
Flea Collar For Cats (Plastic)
Lost and Found Flea Collar For Cats
Big Red Flea Spray
Permethrin Flea Powder
Pump Action Flea Spray
Defest II
Flego
Flea Buster
Rug-de-Bug

Sherley's Tick Preparations

Tick Away

Sherley's Worming Preparations

Worming Syrup
Worming Cream
Multiwormer For Cats
Worming Granules for Cats

Sherley's Vitamins & Tonics

Vionate
Calcium Tablets
Cooling Tablets
Gastrine Tablets

Sherley's Foods

Lactol
Top Form Cat Treats (various flavours)

Sherley's Other Treatments & Accessories

Deodorant Tablets
Breath Freshener Tablets
Cat-a-Med Hairball Remover
Ear Cleaner
Eye Lotion
Spray Away
Swiftie Trainer

Sherley's Grooming Aids

Grooming Spray
Tea Tree Shampoo
Diagnos Anti-Dandruff Shampoo
Diagnos Anti-Itch Shampoo
Diagnos Hypoallergenic Shampoo

Also available, under the 'Beaphar' brand:

Bowl & Bottle Disinfectant
Disinfectant for Cats
Flea & Tick Spot-on for cats
Herbal Cat Flea Repellent Collar
Herbal Flea Repellent Drop-on
Malt Bits
Vit Bits
Catnip Bits

USEFUL ADDRESSES

The Governing Council for the Cat Fancy (GCCF)
4-6 Penel Orlieu, Bridgwater, Somerset, TA6 3PG.
Telephone: 01278 427575
Register for pedigree cats and is the main ruling body for cat shows. Contact for any issues about pedigree cats, including welfare, buying and selling, and locating.

The Cat Association
Mill House, Letcombe Regis, Oxon, OX12 9JD.
Telephone: 01235 766543
The British member of Fife, the world-wide cat show/breed body. It is a registration and show organisation - most CA shows are international.

Cats Protection League (CPL)
17 King's Road, Horsham, West Sussex, RH13 5PN.
Telephone: 01403 221900

CPL HELPLINE: 01403 221919
Britain's largest cat charity aims to rescue stray and unwanted cats and rehome where possible. They have 13 shelters and a network of 240 branches throughout Britain.

Association of Pet Behaviour Counsellors
P O Box 46, Worcester, WR8 9YS.
Telephone: 01386 751151
Contact to obtain the name of a local behaviour counsellor to whom you can be referred after consultation with a Veterinary Surgeon. A useful publications list is also available.

People's Dispensary for Sick Animals (PDSA)
Whitechapel Way, Priorslee, Telford, Shropshire, TF2 9PQ.
Telephone: 01952 290999
Britain's largest veterinary charity providing free treatment for the sick pets of needy owners.

Royal Society for the Prevention of Cruelty to Animals (RSPCA)
Wilberforce Way, Southwater, Horsham, West Sussex, RH13 9RS.
Telephone: 0870 3335999

Royal Society for the prevention of Cruelty to Animals (RSPCA) National Helpline
Telephone: 0870 5555999

Pet Bereavement Helpline
(Run by the Society for Companion Animal Studies, 10b Leny Road, Callander, Scotland, FK17 8BA)
Produces a very useful booklet entitled "Death of an Animal Friend" and runs a befriender service for bereaved pet-owners.
Helpline Number: 0800 0966606

The Feline Advisory Bureau (FAB)
Taeselbury, High Street, Tisbury, Wiltshire, SP3 6LD.
Telephone: 0870 7422278
FAB is a charity dedicated to the health and welfare of cats, promoting pioneering Veterinary work. It brings together information on the treatment, care, welfare, and the management of cats, and makes it available to vets, breeders, cattery proprietors and cat owners. Leaflets are produced on health topics and common behaviour problems. The FAB also runs boarding cattery services, including assessment, training courses, and publishes a list of approved catteries.

NOTES

NOTES

NOTES